IDENTIFICATIO

British & European Mushrooms & Other Fungi

Publisher and Creative Director: Nick Wells
Project Editor: Sara Robson
Picture Research: Gemma Walters
Consultant Naturalist: Chris McLaren
Art Director: Mike Spender
Digital Design and Production: Chris Herbert
Layout Design: Cliff O'Dea

Special thanks to: Chelsea Edwards, Julie Pallot, Julia Rolf, Helen Tovey and Claire Walker

07 09 11 10 08

1 3 5 7 9 10 8 6 4 2

This edition first published 2007 by
FLAME TREE PUBLISHING
Crabtree Hall, Crabtree Lane
Fulham, London SW6 6TY
United Kingdom

www.flametreepublishing.com

Flame Tree Publishing is part of the Foundry Creative Media Co. Ltd.

ISBN 978-1-84451-930-9

A CIP record for this book is available from the British Library upon request.

Printed in China

IDENTIFICATION GUIDES

British & European Mushrooms & Other Fungi

Eleanor Lawrence and Sue Harniess

FLAME TREE PUBLISHING

Contents

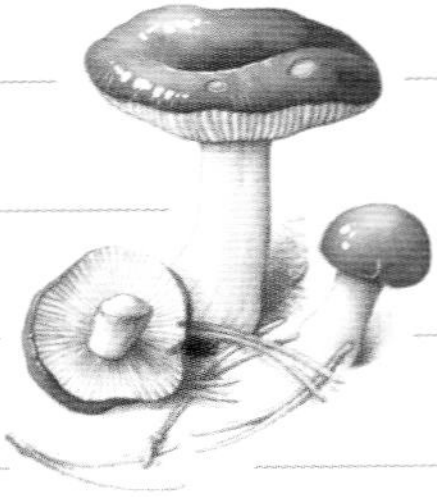

Introduction

Fungi are amongst the most fascinating members of the vegetable kingdom. Traditionally regarded as plants, they are now placed by biologists in a kingdom of their own. Unlike green plants they contain no chlorophyll and cannot make their own food using the sun's energy. Instead they extract nourishment from the soil or from a wood or other material on which they live, causing it slowly to rot away. They are the most important part of the great cycle of life, releasing elements locked in dead animal and plant matter to be returned to the soil and used again.

There are many thousands of species of fungi, some so small they are only visible under the microscope. In this book we present a selection of the larger fungi, including many that are gathered for food and those deadly poisonous species that must be avoided at all costs.

Identifying fungi for the table requires great care. If you are a complete novice do not rely entirely on books but also get your finds identified by someone knowledgeable. A good way to start is to go on an organized mushroom hunt with a local mycological society or mushroom club.

Always check very carefully that a mushroom you think is edible corresponds in all respects to its description in the book. A difference in spore colour, for example, could mean that you have gathered a poisonous species. **If you are at all unsure, do not eat it!** Before you go out collecting, look through the whole book and familiarize yourself with the better-known edible and

poisonous species and note the ones that can be confused. Always gather the complete mushroom, including the very base of the stalk, so that you have all the parts needed to make an identification. Where possible also gather several of the same species at different stages of development. Collect mushrooms in a wide, flat-bottomed basket, not in plastic bags in which they become easily damaged and identifying features lost. Finally, when trying a new species for the first time, only eat a very little of it, as even edible mushrooms can cause illness and allergies in some susceptible people. Always keep one of the mushrooms in case it has to be identified by experts later.

All the mushrooms noted as edible in this book are common species that have been eaten for many years. Those not designated as either edible or poisonous should be regarded as inedible.

Very few mushrooms have familiar common names, and common names also vary widely from place to place and from book to book. Since it is so important to be sure exactly which mushroom one is dealing with, the Latin name has also been included in each case. Although these may seem offputting at first it is well worth getting to know them as it is then much easier to check your finds with an expert or with other books.

How to Use this Book

The book has been divided into five main sections indicating the type of habitat in which certain mushrooms are most likely to be found. Each habitat is indicated by a different colour (see Contents on p.4). Some mushrooms grow in a close relationship with the roots of certain trees and are only found in association with them. Others, although they prefer a certain type of habitat, may also be found elsewhere. The five sections are:

Broad-leaved Woodland

Most commonly found growing on the ground in broad-leaved woodland or in association with broad-leaved trees such as beech, birch and oak.

Coniferous Woodland

Most commonly found growing on the ground in coniferous woods or forests or in association with conifers such as pine and spruce.

Mixed Woodland

May be found growing on the ground in mixed woodland or in association with either coniferous or broad-leaved trees.

Grasslands and Parks

Most typically found in grass or open situations, as in lawns, pasture, parks, gardens, roadsides, woodland glades, waste places, heaths or moors.

Growing on Wood

Growing directly on wood, as on living trees, stumps, cut timber, rotting wood or twigs and branches on the ground.

Within each main section fungi have been placed into subsections possessing certain identification features in common. These groups have been chosen to identify the species illustrated in this book only and do not necessarily reflect biological relationships. Within each section these subsections are identified by symbols (see p.13).

Identification Features

Mushrooms are the fruiting bodies of certain sorts of fungi. The fungus lives for most of the year as a mass of thin threads known as a mycelium, which is often visible as a cottony mass at the base of the stalk. At the appropriate time of year, in late summer and autumn for most mushrooms, this mycelium produces fruiting bodies containing spores by which the fungus propagates itself.

In some mushrooms the spores are borne on thin leaf-like gills on the underside of the cap (see Fig. 1 on p.10) in others (boletes, polypores and relatives) they are formed in close-packed tubes that take the place of the gills.

Important features to look for are the shape of the cap (see Fig. 2 on p.10), whether the mushroom has a ring or volva on the stalk (see Fig. 1 on p.10), and how the gills are attached to the stalk (see Fig. 3 on p.11). Not all mushrooms have all the features shown. Many mushrooms do not, for example, have a ring or a volva. In some mushrooms, such as cortinarias (corts), the young gills are covered by a cobwebby veil, the cortina, which sometimes leaves traces on the stalk and edge of cap. Always handle mushrooms carefully when gathering them to preserve the surface texture of the cap and stalk, which are also useful in identification.

Parts of a Mushroom

FIG. 1

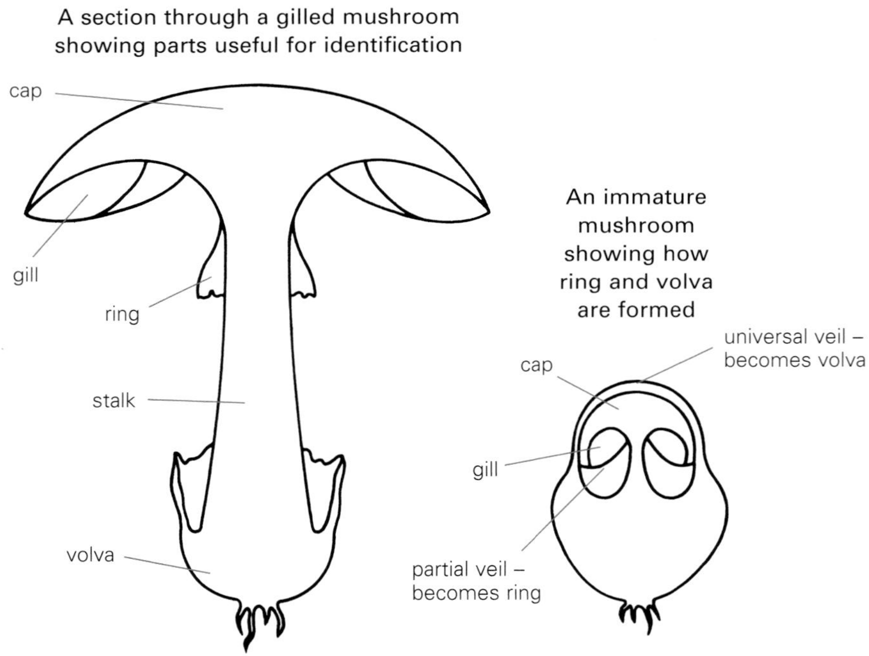

Types of Cap Shape

FIG. 2

Types of Gill Attachment

FIG. 3

Taking a Spore Print

The colour of the spores is also an important identifying feature, helping to divide mushrooms into several large groups, and to distinguish between rather similar mushrooms belonging to different groups. To take a spore print the mushroom is cut off just below the cap and placed on a sheet of white paper (or black paper if you suspect you will get a white spore print). A glass or a plastic bag is placed over it. After a period ranging from a few hours to a day, spores will drop from the gills or pores to make a print on the paper.

Identification Symbols

Within each section fungi with certain features in common have been grouped together, and each group is identified by the following symbol at the top of the left-hand page.

Fungi with teeth or ridges on undersurface, not gills or pores
e.g. Horn of Plenty, Chanterelle, Bear's Head Tooth.

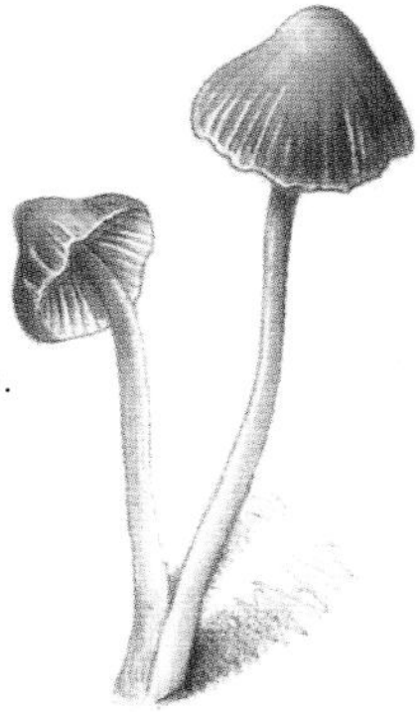

Fungi with pores on underside of a cap or a bracket
Central stem and rounded cap, growing on ground. These are the boletes.

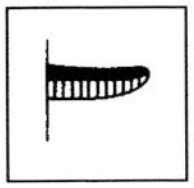

Fungi with very short or no stalk, or shelf-like, growing on wood
e.g. polypores, Turkey Tail.

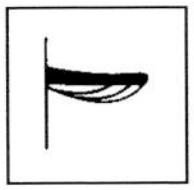

Fungi with gills on underside of a cap or bracket
No or very short stalk, or shelf-like, growing on wood, e.g. Oyster Mushroom.

Typical mushroom-like fungi with gills on the underside of a cap and a central stalk
Small fragile mushrooms, generally no more than 6 cm ($2^1/_2$ in) high with a delicate cap. Cap generally convex, hemispherical, or conical, e.g. mycenas, psilocybes.

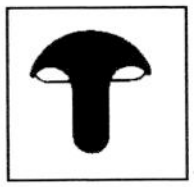

More robust mushrooms with gills that reach the stem (i.e. attached gills), and no ring or volva, e.g. russulas, trichs, milk-caps, and many others.

More robust mushrooms with attached gills, no volva, possessing a cobwebby veil (the cortina) over gills in young specimens, sometimes leaving a ring-like mark, or series of marks, on stalk, e.g. corts.

More robust mushrooms with ring on stalk, no volva, and attached gills, e.g. agrocybes, Honey Fungus, Gypsy.

More robust mushrooms with no ring or volva on stem, gills do not reach stalk (free gills), e.g. Fawn Mushroom.

Larger mushrooms with no ring on stem but which have a volva and free gills, e.g. volvariellas.

Larger mushrooms with free gills, a ring on stalk, but no volva or with volva reduced to scales at base of stalk, e.g. agarics, some amanitas, lepiotas.

Larger mushrooms with free gills and both ring and volva, e.g. some amanitas.

Fungi without teeth, gills or pores, fruitbodies not in typical mushroom shape, e.g. stinkhorn, morels, puffballs, earthstars, earthballs, coral-fungi.

After having determined the section in which your mushroom is likely to be, look at the illustrated pages giving detailed descriptions of each species. The size is indicated at the top of each left-hand page by measurements for cap diameter and length of stalk (see Fig. 4 on p.16).

Four paragraphs of text provide information for identification. The first paragraph, under **Primary Features**, gives features which together with the illustration should enable you to distinguish that species from others illustrated in this book and wherever possible from others which you might come across, especially poisonous species. The second paragraph, under **Other Features**, gives supplementary information to help identification, and notes on edibility or otherwise.

Habitat and Distribution of the illustrated mushrooms are given in the third paragraph, and the fourth paragraph, under **Lookalikes**, gives species with which they might be confused. Those in **bold type** are illustrated elsewhere in this book.

There are more than a thousand species of larger fungi in Europe, and so you will inevitably find fungi not illustrated in this book. Nevertheless, you will be able to identify some of them to their family group or *genus*, such as *Agaricus*, *Russula* or *Lactarius*, by noting the spore colour, type of attachment of the gills etc., and looking for similar species in these pages. However, **do not eat anything you have not identified precisely**, as a single genus can contain both edible and poisonous species.

Warning Symbol

Throughout this book this sign has been used to indicate that a mushroom is toxic, indigestible or has a highly disagreeable taste, and should never be eaten. Some mushrooms are deadly and therefore the reader is advised to take great care in identification of all types.

If in any doubt DO NOT EAT!
Always consult an expert!

Specimen Spread

FIG. 4

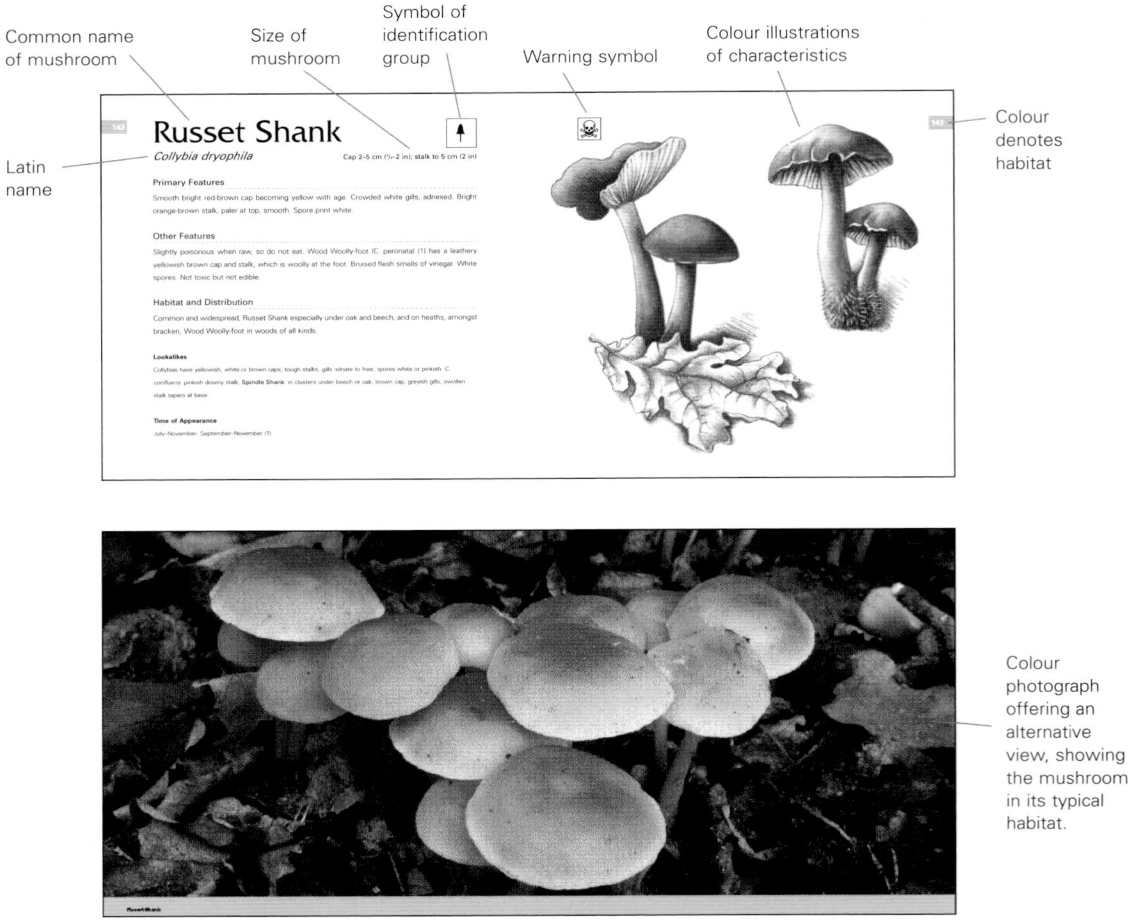

Common name of mushroom
Size of mushroom
Symbol of identification group
Warning symbol
Colour illustrations of characteristics
Latin name
Colour denotes habitat
Russet Shank
Collybia dryophila
Cap 2–5 cm (3/4–2 in); stalk to 5 cm (2 in)
Primary Features
Smooth bright red-brown cap becoming yellow with age. Crowded white gills, adnexed. Bright orange-brown stalk, paler at top, smooth. Spore print white.
Other Features
Slightly poisonous when raw, so do not eat. Wood Woolly-foot (C. peronata) (1) has a leathery yellowish brown cap and stalk, which is woolly at the foot. Bruised flesh smells of vinegar. White spores. Not toxic but not edible.
Habitat and Distribution
Common and widespread, Russet Shank especially under oak and beech, and on heaths, amongst bracken, Wood Woolly-foot in woods of all kinds.
Lookalikes
Collybias have yellowish, white or brown caps, tough stalks, gills adnate to free, spores white or pinkish. C. confluens: pinkish downy stalk; Spindle Shank: in clusters under beech or oak, brown cap, greyish gills, swollen stalk tapers at base.
Time of Appearance
July–November; September–November (1)
Colour photograph offering an alternative view, showing the mushroom in its typical habitat.

Horn of Plenty

Craterellus cornucopioides Cap 5–15 cm (2–6 in); height to 12 cm (4¾ in)

Primary Features

Blackish or dark grey-brown, narrow funnel-shaped cap with a flared wavy lip. Outer surface of cap is smooth or faintly ridged, the inner surface slightly scaly or velvety.

Other Features

A small to medium-sized vase-shaped fungus with a short hollow stem and thin greyish flesh. Spores white. One form has a yellow outer surface. Good to eat and can be dried and stored.

Habitat and Distribution

Under broad-leaved trees, especially oak and beech, often in clusters. Relatively common throughout Europe.

Lookalikes

The similar *Cantharellus cinereus* has well-defined forked ridges on outer surface. Although no vase-shaped fungus with ridges on underside is toxic, take great care not to confuse them with similar-shaped species with true gills.

Time of Appearance

August–November

Be careful not to confuse the vase-shaped Horn of Plenty fungus, with its underside ridges, with similar species that have true gills, as the latter may be toxic.

Spring Bolete

Boletus reticulatus (aestivalis) Cap 12–25 cm ($4\frac{3}{4}$–10 in); stalk to 15 cm (6 in)

Primary Features

Uniform pale-brown to brown matt surface to cap, and pores remaining whitish for a long time. Stem reddish brown covered all over with a distinct fine white network.

Other Features

A typical bolete, with a fleshy cap whose surface tends to crack, and thick stem swelling towards the base. The colour of the pores remains unchanged when bruised. The flesh is white and firm. Good to eat, with a sweet nutty taste.

Habitat and Distribution

Under broad-leaved trees, especially beech. Appearing earlier in the year than the Cep.

Lookalikes

Cep and other boletes; **Bitter Bolete**, **inedible**; **Satan's Bolete** *(B. satanas)* **(1)**: **toxic**, pale-grey cap, red pores, bright red network on a stem swollen at base; *B. fragrans*: dark-brown cap, strong fruity scent, **edibility doubtful**.

Time of Appearance

May–October

1

Brown Birch Bolete

Krombholziella scabra

Cap 8–13 cm (3¼–5¼ in); stalk to 15 cm (6 in)

Primary Features

Rough stalk covered with hard small brown or black scales. Cap greyish brown to dark brown, pores off-white to buff. Flesh unchanging when cut, or bruising slightly brownish.

Other Features

A tall-stalked bolete with a cap dry, greasy or sticky to the touch, starting convex and sometimes becoming flatter with a depression in centre. Pores change from pale buff to greyish with age. Edible and good.

Habitat and Distribution

Under broad-leaved trees, especially birch. Widely distributed and quite common throughout Europe.

Lookalikes

Several scaly stalked boletes grow in association with broad-leaved trees. They differ in cap colour and texture, and in the discoloration of the flesh on cutting. None is poisonous, the **Red-capped Bolete** being considered the best to eat.

Time of Appearance

June/July–November

The Brown Birch Bolete is a tall-stalked edible bolete. The convex cap sometimes becomes flatter, with a depression in the centre, with age.

Red-Cracked Bolete

Xerocomus chrysenteron

Cap 8–12 cm ($3\frac{1}{4}$–$4\frac{3}{4}$ in); stalk to 6 cm ($2\frac{1}{2}$ in)

Primary Features

The dull olive-brown skin of the cap becomes cracked, showing a pink layer underneath. Pores dirty yellow to greenish. Flesh yellow, sometimes turning blue or green on bruising.

Other Features

Medium-sized bolete, with stalk slightly bent towards the foot. The **Yellow-cracked Bolete** *(X. subtomentuosus)* **(1)** has a velvety pale-buff to olive-brown cap, becoming cracked, golden pores and a cream stalk. Both edible.

Habitat and Distribution

Under broad-leaved trees, in grassy copses. Both are common throughout most of Europe.

Lookalikes

Other *Xerocomus* species occur under broad-leaved trees, with brown or red caps, sometimes cracking, but no others show pink flesh underneath. One species is parasitic on earthballs. The **Bay Bolete** grows under conifers.

Time of Appearance

August–November

1

The Red-cracked Bolete, easily identified by the colouring of its cap, is commonly found under broad-leaved trees throughout Europe.

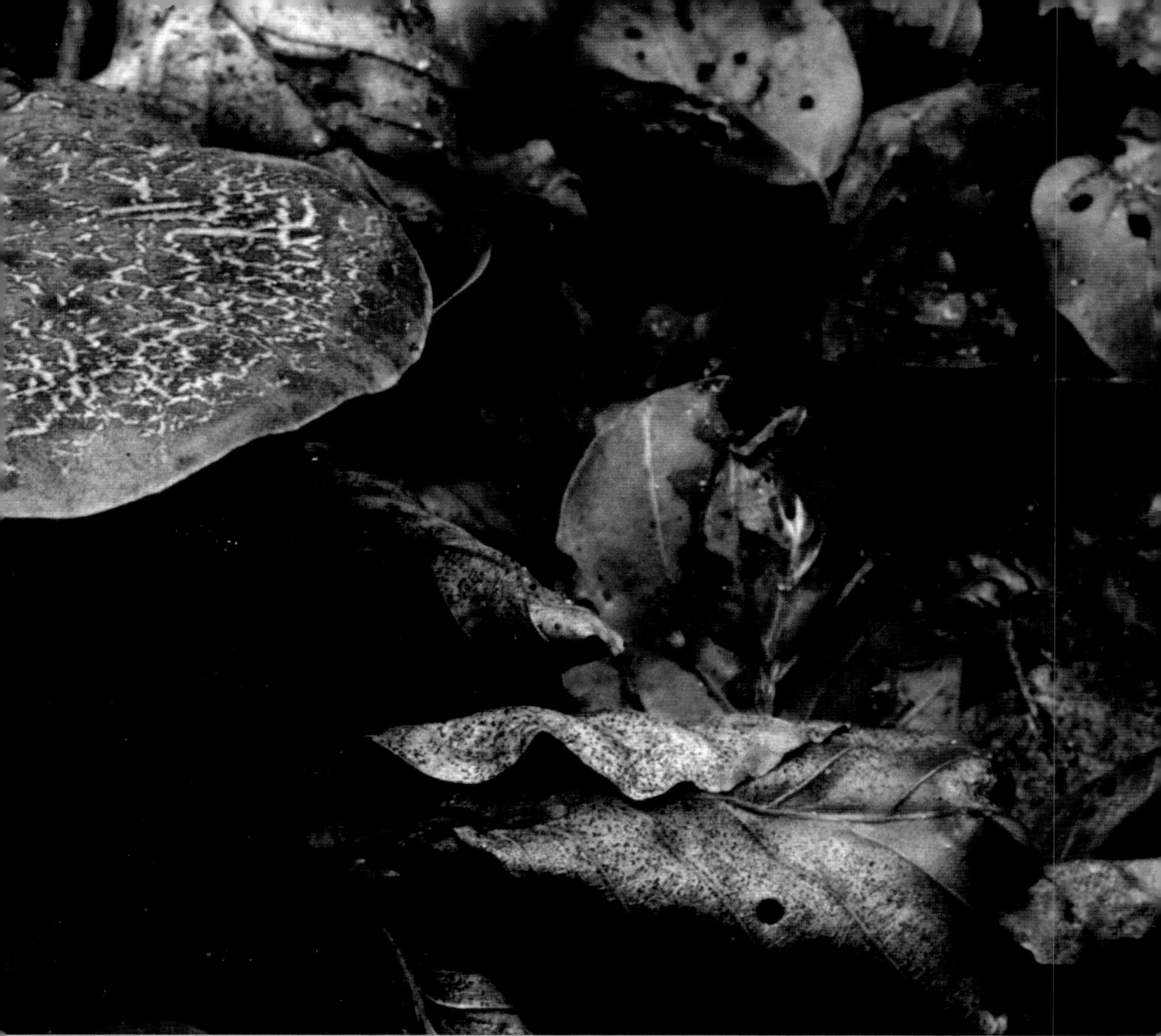

Chestnut Bolete

Gyroporus castaneus

Cap 5–10 cm (2–4 in); stalk to 10 cm (4 in)

Primary Features

Small bolete with rusty-brown to chestnut cap, white or pale-yellow pores, not changing colour when bruised. Stalk same colour or paler than cap, rather uneven, brittle and hollow.

Other Features

The surface of the rounded fleshy cap is smooth or slightly velvety and the stalk also has a slight bloom when young. The white flesh does not change colour when cut. **Edibility suspect**.

Habitat and Distribution

Under broad-leaved trees, especially oak and beech, often growing in clusters. Quite common and widespread.

Lookalikes

Bluing Bolete; **Ceps** and other **boletes**; **Slippery Jack** and other *Suillus* spp.

Time of Appearance

August–October

The cap of the small Chestnut Bolete is smooth or slightly velvety to the touch. It often grows in clusters beneath oak and beech trees.

Green-Cracked Russula

Cap 10–15 cm (4–6 in); stalk to 5 cm (2 in)

Russula virescens

Primary Features

Brittle gills and flesh typical of a russula. Pale-green or bluish-green matt cap surface flaking and cracking to show white underneath. Creamy-white gills. White spores.

Other Features

Flesh hard and white, spongy in the stalk. Edible, with a mild nutty taste. **Forked-gill Russula** *(R. cyanoxantha)* (**1**) cap is bluish green to violet, not cracking. The gills are distinctly forked. Edible, good.

Habitat and Distribution

In broadland woods, especially beech. Both are widespread and common.

Lookalikes

Green Russula: gills forked but more crowded; *R. cutefracta* has a darker-green or bronze-tinted cap, cracking inwards from the edge. Edible, although some forms may be acrid.

Time of Appearance

July/August–November

Other Russulas

Green Russula *(R.heterophylla)* (**1**) has smooth shiny-green to bronze cap, 8–15 cm ($3\frac{1}{4}$–6 in) across, crowded white gills, forked. Spore print white. Edible, but take care to distinguish from the deadly **Death Cap**.

Bare-Toothed Russula *(R. vesca)* (**2**) has a pinky-brown cap, 5–9 cm (2–$3\frac{1}{2}$ in) across, becoming dull yellow in centre. Skin peels off easily and mature specimens show white flesh at edge of cap where skin has retracted. Spore print white.

Golden Russula *(R. aurea)* (**3**) is one of many bright red-capped russulas found in broad-leaved and mixed woods. It has a brick-red cap and bright-yellow gills and flesh. It prefers warmer areas. Spore print ochre to yellow.

1

2

3

Milk-Caps

(Lactarius)

The many different species of Milk-cap look similar to russulas but the gills release a milky fluid when broken. All have a white spore print. Many are hot and peppery to the taste, but a few are edible.

Slimy Milk-cap *(L. blennius)* (**1**): cap 6–10 cm (2¼–4 in) across, olive brown to grey green, often with concentric rings of drop-like marks around edge, and becoming sticky and slippery when wet. Milk turns grey on exposure to air. Flesh very acrid. Under beech.

Sweet Milk-cap *(L. subdulcis)* (**2**): cap 3–6 cm (1¼–2½ in) across, pinkish tan, with a surface like suede leather. Gills pale cream or tinged pink, stalk cream at top becoming brown lower down. The milk stays white. Mild taste. Edible. Common under beech and other broad-leaved trees.

Oak Milk-cap *(L. quietus)* (**3**): cap 6–10 cm (2½–4 in), dull reddish brown with darker zones. Gills creamy. Milk white. Flesh has a smell sometimes described as 'like wet linen'. Under oak. **Inedible**.

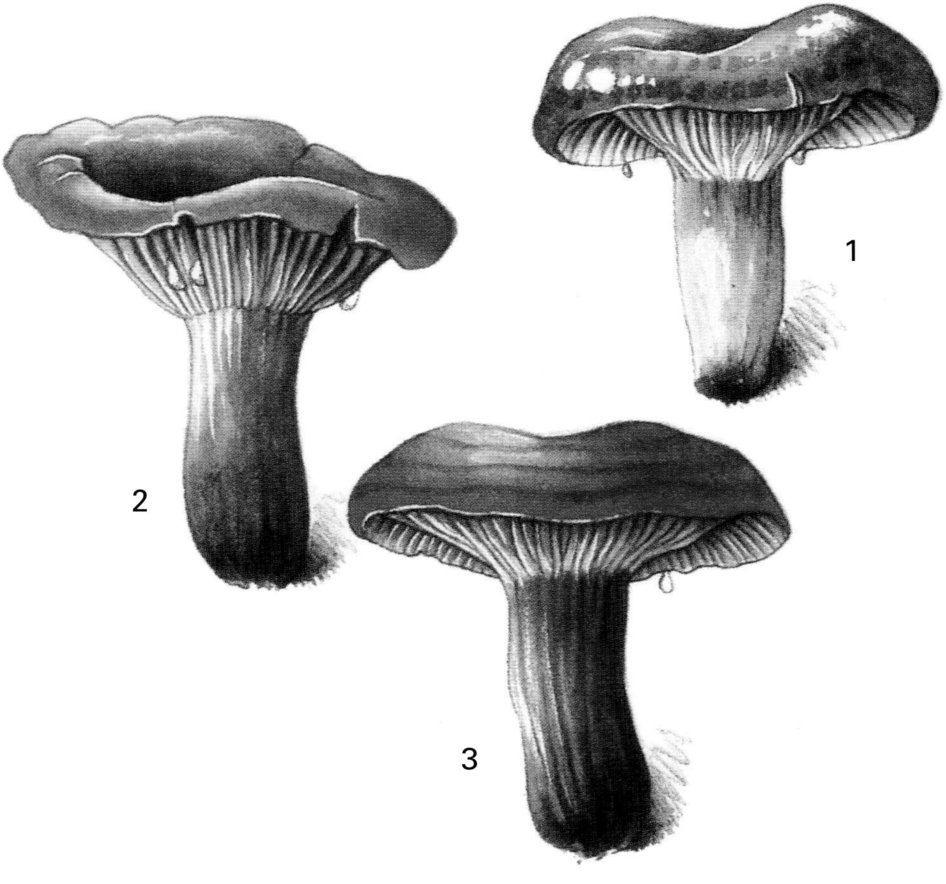
1
2
3

Peppery Milk-Cap

Lactarius piperatus

Cap 6–12 cm ($2\frac{1}{2}$–$4\frac{3}{4}$ in); stalk to 8 cm ($3\frac{1}{4}$ in)

Primary Features

White cap becoming sunken in centre. Cream or slightly pinkish crowded gills exude a copious, very acrid milk, which stays white. White stalk does not discolour on bruising.

Other Features

Cap has a matt, wrinkled surface and edge rolled under. The gills run down the stalk slightly. **Voluminous-latex Milk-cap** *(L. volemus)* (**1**) has a pale-orange, matt, wrinkled cap, crowded yellow gills and smells fishy when handled. Edible.

Habitat and Distribution

Peppery Milk-cap: broad-leaved copses on neutral or limy soil. Voluminous-latex Milk-cap: especially under oak.

Lookalikes

Other white milk-caps include *L. vellereus* which is larger (12–35 cm or $4\frac{3}{4}$–14 in across) with a lobed edge to cap and short stout stalk; other white or grey milk-caps have milk changing colour or shorter stalks. None is edible.

Time of Appearance

August–November

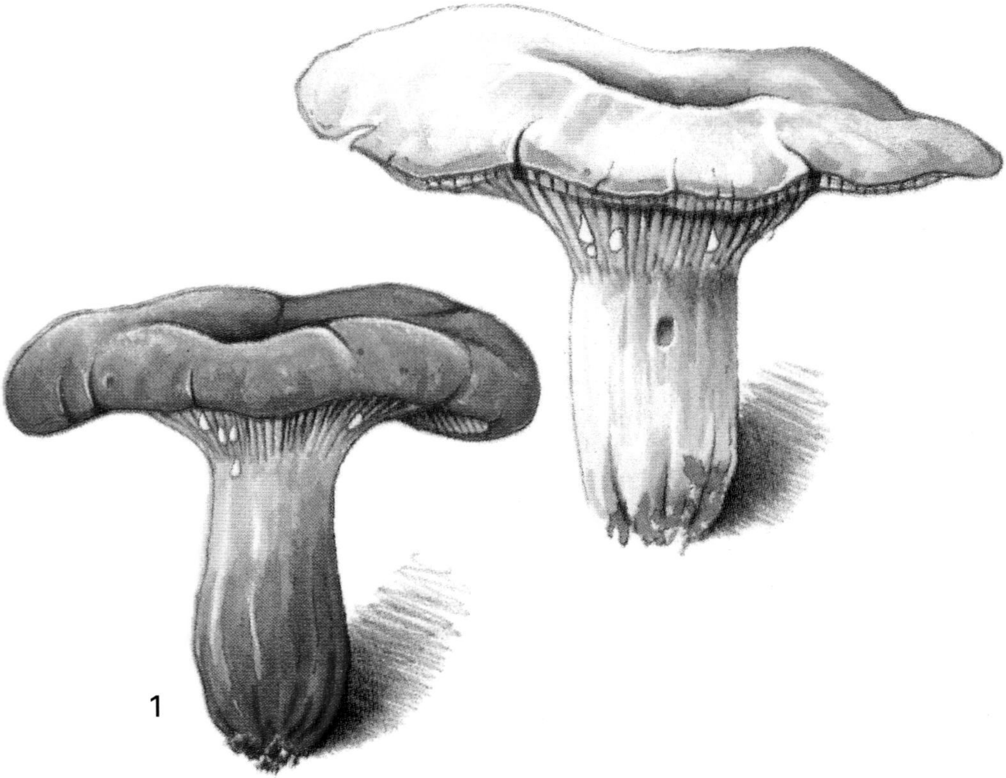

1

The Peppery Milk-cap has a rolled-under edge to its cap and its gills run slightly down its stalk. It is the only edible white milk-cap.

Woolly Milk-Cap

Lactarius torminosus

Cap 8–12 cm ($3\frac{1}{4}$–$4\frac{3}{4}$ in); stalk to 8 cm ($3\frac{1}{4}$ in)

Primary Features

Cap pinkish to flesh coloured, with concentric paler zones. The incurved edge is very shaggy or woolly. Pinkish gills release a white unchanging acrid milk. Spore print cream.

Other Features

White flesh smells faintly of geranium leaves. Stem white, pitted pink. **Inedible, considered poisonous**. ***L. chrysorrheus*** (**1**) has a smooth cap with a yellowish tinge and gills and stem bruises yellow. Acrid but edible after cooking.

Habitat and Distribution

Woolly Milk-cap: under birch, often in mixed woods and on heaths, common. *L. chrysorrheus:* common under broad-leaved trees, especially oak.

Lookalikes

Saffron Milk-cap: in conifer woods.

Time of Appearance

August–November

1

The Woolly Milk-cap is named after the very woolly edge of its cap. Its white flesh smells faintly of geranium leaves, and is considered poisonous.

The Miller

Clitopilus prunulus

Cap 5–12 cm (2–4¾ in); stalk to 3 cm (1¼ in)

Primary Features

White velvety cap often becoming sunken in centre, with lobed incurved edge, and pink gills descending a white stalk. Strong smell of new-ground wheatmeal. Spore print pink.

Other Features

The lobed edge to cap is more marked in older specimens. Gills are cream at first. The thick white stalk is sometimes placed off-centre. A good edible fungus but may be confused with several poisonous species (see below).

Habitat and Distribution

Common and widespread under various broad-leaved trees, often on heaths or in grassland.

Lookalikes

Sweating Mushroom, poisonous; Lead Poisoner, poisonous; Field Mushroom and other *Agaricus* spp, ring on stalk, gills free; St George's Mushroom.

Time of Appearance

July–November

Deadly Inocybe

Inocybe patouillardii

Cap 3–7 cm ($1\frac{1}{4}$–$2\frac{3}{4}$ in); stalk to 8 cm ($3\frac{1}{4}$ in)

Primary Features

Silky-whitish conical to bell-shaped cap with a lobed edge becomes a dull orange with age. Gills, flesh and cap surface redden on bruising. Stout white stalk. Spore print brown.

Other Features

The cap edge often splits towards the centre as it expands. This mushroom is **deadly poisonous**. It has a fruity smell which becomes earthy.

Habitat and Distribution

At the edges of broad-leaved woods and under broad-leaved trees in parks and gardens.

Lookalikes

I. adequate: silky dark-brown, twisted fibrous stalk; *I. rimosa*: fawn with darker silky fibrils, gills yellowish green; *I. maculata*: nut brown with white patches at centre of cap, gills beige. All spore prints brown.

Time of Appearance

May–November

Soap-Scented Tricholoma

Cap 10–15 cm (4–6 in); stalk to 12 cm ($4^{3}/_{4}$ in)

Tricholoma saponaceum

Primary Features

Fleshy fungus with a dark-grey to grey-brown cap, gills far apart, sinuate (typical of all tricholomas), white or pale yellow. Distinctive soapy smell. Spore print white.

Other Features

Cap smooth and silky, cracking into scales in dry weather. Flesh pale. **Inedible**. **Sulphur Tricholoma** *(T. sulphureum)* (**1**) cap 4–8 cm ($1^{1}/_{2}$–$3^{1}/_{4}$ in) is bright yellow with an unpleasant smell. Gills sinuate-adnexed. White spores. **Poisonous**.

Habitat and Distribution

Soap-scented Tricholoma: widespread and common under broad-leaved trees, also under conifers. Sulphur Tricholoma: locally common, especially under beech, oak and holly.

Lookalikes

Death Cap; **Marvellous Tricholoma**; **White Tricholoma**; **Leopard Tricholoma**; tricholomas are distinguished by their sinuate gills and white spores. **There are several poisonous species**. A few have a ring-like marking on the stalk.

Time of Appearance

August–November

1

Lead Poisoner

Entoloma sinuatum (lividum) Cap 8–20 cm (3¼–8 in); stalk to 12 cm (4¾ in)

Primary Features

One of the larger entolomas. Creamy-yellow to pale-coffee-coloured slippery cap. Gills adnexed, almost free, not crowded, yellowish, turning pink. Silky stalk. Spores pink.

Other Features

Large fleshy fungus with cap edge incurved in young specimens becoming wavy edged when old. The thick white firm flesh smells slightly of cucumber or new-ground meal. **Highly poisonous**, causing cramps, severe vomiting and diarrhoea.

Habitat and Distribution

Widespread under broad-leaved trees, also in parks, wasteland and by roadsides.

Lookalikes

Cloudy Agaric; **St George's Mushroom**; **The Miller** (decurrent gills); other entolomas (sinuate or adnexed gills, pink spores); other tricholomas (sinuate gills, white spores).

Time of Appearance

July–November

Rooted Oudemansiella

Oudemansiella radicata

Cap 3–9 cm ($1\frac{1}{4}$–$3\frac{1}{2}$ in); stalk to 20 cm (8 in)

Primary Features

Tall mushroom with tough slender stalk ending in a long underground 'taproot' eventually contacting wood. Sticky yellowish-brown cap, gills pure white.

Other Features

The cap often has wrinkles radiating out from centre, and thin pale flesh. Gills are thick, spaced far apart, and adnexed. Stem white to brownish, fibrous and twisted. Spore print white.

Habitat and Distribution

Common and widespread in woods, especially under beech and oak.

Lookalikes

The rarer *O. longipes* has a dry, slightly hairy, brownish cap, no taproot, and long, twisted stalk covered in velvety-brown hairs.

Time of Appearance

June–November

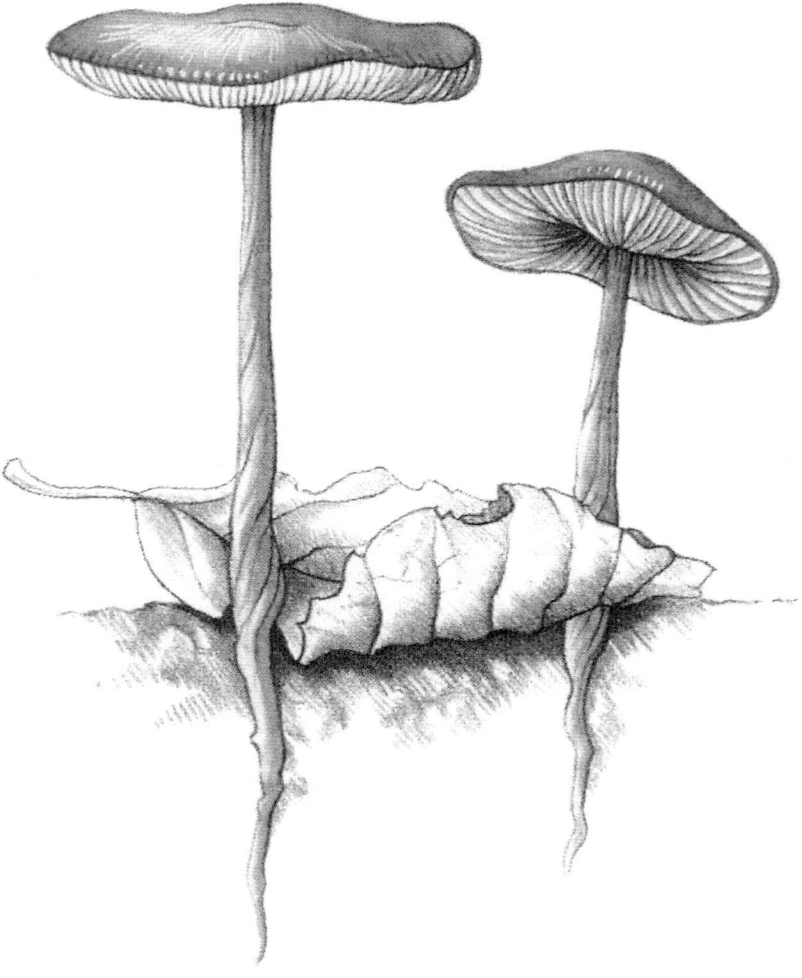

Red-Banded Cortinarius

Cortinarius armillatus

Cap 8–12 cm (3¼–4¾ in); stalk to 12 cm (4¾ in)

Primary Features

Large fleshy mushroom with reddish-brown cap and stalk, the stalk bearing bright-red irregular diagonal bands which are the remnants of a partial veil. Rust-brown spore print.

Other Features

The bell-shaped cap ranges from fawn to dark russet, with a slightly silky surface. Stalk thick, pale russet with a bulbous base. Gills pale brown becoming dark rust. The white cortina leaves a whitish band on upper stalk.

Habitat and Distribution

Widespread and common under birch, on acid soil, especially near damp ground.

Lookalikes

The many species of **Cortinarius** have variously coloured caps but all have rust-brown spores. Gills adnate or sinuate. **None should be eaten** as there are several deadly species.

Time of Appearance

August–October

Grisette

Amanita vaginata

Cap 6–12 cm ($2\frac{1}{2}$–$4\frac{3}{4}$ in); stalk to 12 cm ($4\frac{3}{4}$ in)

Primary Features

Medium to large mushroom on a tall slender white ringless stem, the base enclosed in a white sac-like volva. Dull fawn or greyish cap has a striated edge. Gills and spores white.

Other Features

This is edible after cooking to destroy toxins, but is thin-fleshed. The **Tawny Grisette** *(A. fulva)* (**1**) has a bright-fawn cap and cream gills. Also edible after cooking. **Do not mistake deadly amanitas for these mushrooms**.

Habitat and Distribution

Both are common and widespread under beech, birch and oak, the Grisette also sometimes being found in coniferous woods.

Lookalikes

A. batterae: close-fitting volva, yellowish-grey cap and stalk, rare, under conifers;

amanitas: ring and sac-like volva or volva remnants at base of stalk.

Time of Appearance

June–October; May–October (**1**)

1

The Panther

Amanita pantherina

Cap 6–10 cm ($2\frac{1}{2}$–4 in); stalk to 8 cm ($3\frac{1}{4}$ in)

Primary Features

Red-brown to coffee-coloured cap dotted with white scales. Gills, stalk and ring are pure white. Bracelet-like remains of volva girdle stalk above base.

Other Features

This handsome amanita is **highly poisonous**. **Jonquil Amanita** *(A. junquillea)* (**1**), cap 5–10 cm (2–4 in), has a yellow cap with large irregular white scales and a striated edge, white or lemon stalk, and a fragile ring. **Inedible**.

Habitat and Distribution

Both found under broad-leaved trees, but not common.

Lookalikes

The Blusher: *A. spissa*, dull-brown cap with greyish scales and volva in ridges around base of stalk. Although edible, avoid for fear of confusion with The Panther; **Lemon Amanita**: lemon cap with white scales, edge not striated.

Time of Appearance

July–October; June–October (**1**)

1

The highly poisonous Panther is similar in appearance to the Blusher, which although edible should be avoided for fear of confusion.

Caesar's Mushroom

Amanita caesarea

Cap 10–20 cm (4–8 in); stalk to 12 cm (4¾ in)

Primary Features

Smooth to greasy bright orange-red cap, occasionally bearing a fragment of the white universal veil. Stalk, gills and ring yellow. White sac-like volva at base of stem.

Other Features

An excellent edible mushroom, highly esteemed by the ancient Romans. Flesh is yellow near surface. Spores white.

Habitat and Distribution

Under broad-leaved trees in southern Europe no further north than the limits of vine cultivation. Not found in Britain.

Lookalikes

The more northerly **Fly Agaric** has white patches on cap.

Time of Appearance

July–October

The only similar species to Caesar's Mushroom is the Fly Agaric, which is found further north and which has white patches on its cap.

Death Cap

Amanita phalloides

Cap 6–12 cm ($2\frac{1}{2}$–$4\frac{3}{4}$ in); stalk to 7 cm ($2\frac{3}{4}$ in)

Primary Features

Smooth greenish-yellow to olive cap, sometimes almost white, sometimes bearing remnants of white veil. Gills white. Stalk bears a ring and large white volva. White spores.

Other Features

This handsome mushroom is **deadly poisonous**, even in tiny amounts. It has a sweet smell rapidly becoming sickly. The young fruitbodies or 'eggs' are completely enclosed in a universal white veil. Stalk pale, flushed same colour as cap.

Habitat and Distribution

Widespread and locally common. Mainly under broad-leaved trees, especially beech and oak, but sometimes under conifers.

Lookalikes

Other amanitas. All the deadly amanitas have white spores, white gills, and bear both ring and volva.

Wash your hands thoroughly after handling any of them.

Time of Appearance

July–November

The Death Cap is extremely poisonous, even in small amounts, hence its name.

Destroying Angels

Amanita virosa

Cap 6–10 cm (2$\frac{1}{2}$–4 in); stalk to 15 cm (6 in)

Primary Features

A shining pure-white mushroom, occasionally with a pink tinge to cap, with a flaring fragile ring and large volva at base of stalk. White crowded gills. White spores.

Other Features

The slightly greasy cap and scaly stalk distinguish this **deadly poisonous** amanita from the **equally deadly** all-white ***A. verna*** **(1)** which has a faint-greenish tinge to the centre of the cap. **Wash hands** thoroughly after handling.

Habitat and Distribution

Both are rather uncommon, *A. virosa* being found under beech, birch and oak and also in mixed woods, *A. verna* being more common in mountains in southern Europe.

Lookalikes

Young specimens can be confused with edible mushroom *(Agaricus)* species; **Death Cap** (white form); **avoid all-white mushrooms** as they include several deadly species; **White Tricholoma**: no ring or volva, white spores.

Time of Appearance

August–October

1

Destroying Angels are just one of several all-white mushrooms that should not be eaten, as several of them are deadly poisonous species.

Common Morel

Morchella esculenta

Cap 3–7 cm ($1\frac{1}{4}$–$2\frac{3}{4}$ in) high; stalk to 17 cm ($6\frac{3}{4}$ in)

Primary Features

Rounded oval cap with a surface like a honeycomb, not separable from stalk at lower edge. Light yellowish brown to grey brown. Stalk whitish, soon becoming hollow.

Other Features

One of the best-known edible fungi which should, however, be eaten with caution as it disagrees with some people. The related **Fluted White Helvella** *(Helvella crispa)* **(1)** and similar fungi are not regarded as edible and are **toxic** raw.

Habitat and Distribution

Common Morel: sandy copses of broad-leaved trees, also on rubbish heaps. Fluted White Helvella: damp broad-leaved woods.

Lookalikes

Forms of the common morel with conical caps are sometimes considered as separate species.

False Morel: **poisonous**; *Mitrophora semilibera*: cap edge free from stalk, edible;

Verpa species: rare, smooth cap 1–2 cm ($\frac{1}{2}$–$\frac{3}{4}$ in) across.

Time of Appearance

April–June; spring and August–October **(1)**

1

Black Truffle

Tuber melanosporum

Fruitbody 6–12 cm ($2\frac{1}{2}$–$4\frac{3}{4}$ in) diameter

Primary Features

Fruitbody grows completely underground. Shining knobbly coal-black outer surface, interior brown flesh marbled with white. Strong fragrance.

Other Features

The most highly prized of all fungi. Specially trained dogs are used to search them out. The **White Truffle** *(T. blottii (aestivum))* (**1**) is paler, and is covered with regular pyramidal warts. It is also edible but less good.

Habitat and Distribution

Black Truffle: uncommon, found in southern Europe, e.g. southern France and Italy, under oaks, in hilly areas. Not found in Britain. White Truffle: found also in Britain, under beech.

Lookalikes

There are several other species of truffle, which are harmless, but of no culinary interest.

Time of Appearance

August–October

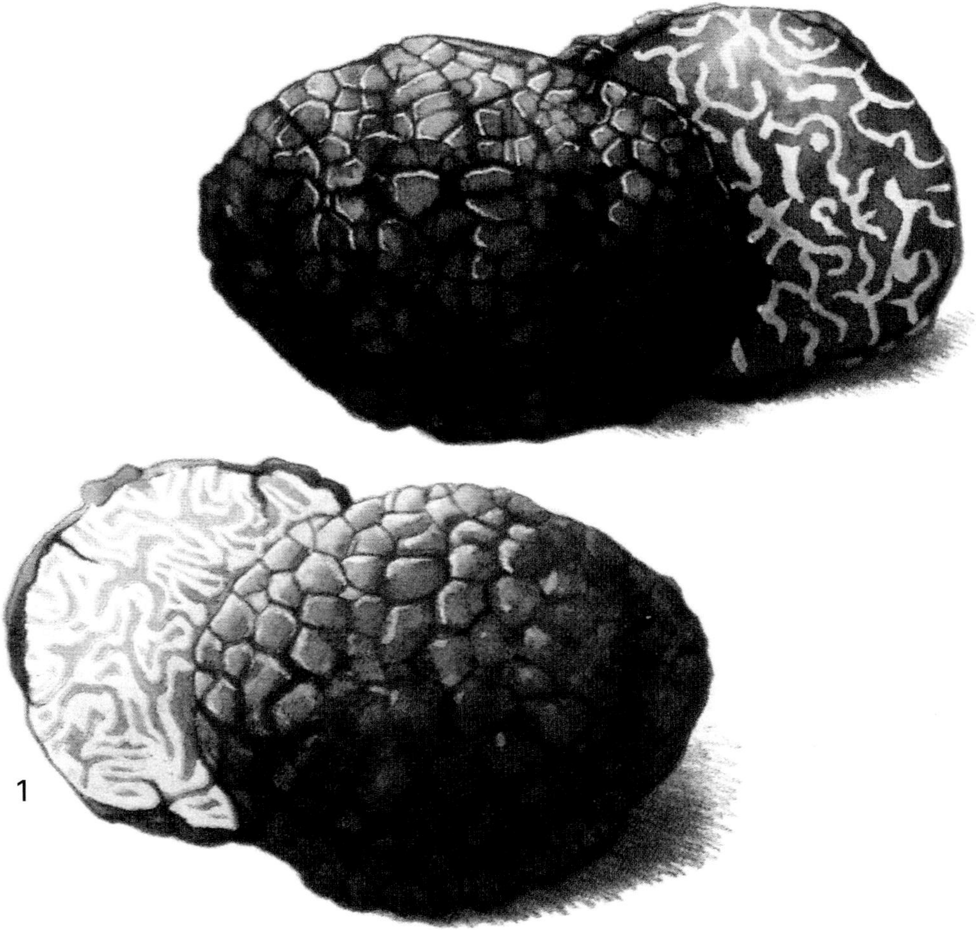

1

Slippery Jack

Suillus luteus

Cap 8–13 cm ($3\frac{1}{4}$–$5\frac{1}{4}$ in); stalk to 6 cm ($2\frac{1}{2}$ in)

Primary Features

Dark-brown slimy cap with tiny yellow pores on underside, and a white ring on stalk.

Other Features

The stalk is often covered with brownish granules above the ring, becoming white or brown below. The thick flesh is pale yellow and does not change colour when bruised. Good to eat if the slime is first removed.

Habitat and Distribution

Common and widespread, especially under pines.

Lookalikes

Suillus spp have slimy caps. *S. granulatus*: pale-brown cap, pores exude fluid, no ring, edible after peeling; *S. bovinus:* yellowish cap, large pores, no ring, **inedible**; *S. grevillei:* under larch, golden-yellow cap, ring, **inedible**.

Time of Appearance

July–November

The Slippery Jack is good to eat if peeled, as its dark-brown cap is slimy. There are several other *Suillus* species, only some of which are edible.

Yellow-Stemmed Mycena

Mycena epipterygia

Cap 1–2 cm ($^{1}/_{2}$–$^{3}/_{4}$ in); stalk to 10 cm (4 in)

Primary Features

Delicate pale-brown mushroom with a bell-shaped slimy cap, striated at the edge, and a slender, yellowish slimy stalk. Spore print white.

Other Features

Gills white with a yellow tinge. **Nitrous Mycena** *(M. leptocephala)* (**1**), growing in clusters on pine needles, is not slimy, cap opens out more and is greyer. Stalk grey. Gills pale, spores white.

Habitat and Distribution

Both are very common and widespread under conifers.

Lookalikes

Milk-drop Mycena and many other small brown mycenas. *M. sanguinolenta*: stem exudes a red juice. Mycenas have fibrous stems, attached gills, often sinuate, and white spores. Cap colour ranges from brown to white, pink, lilac or yellow.

Time of Appearance

September–November

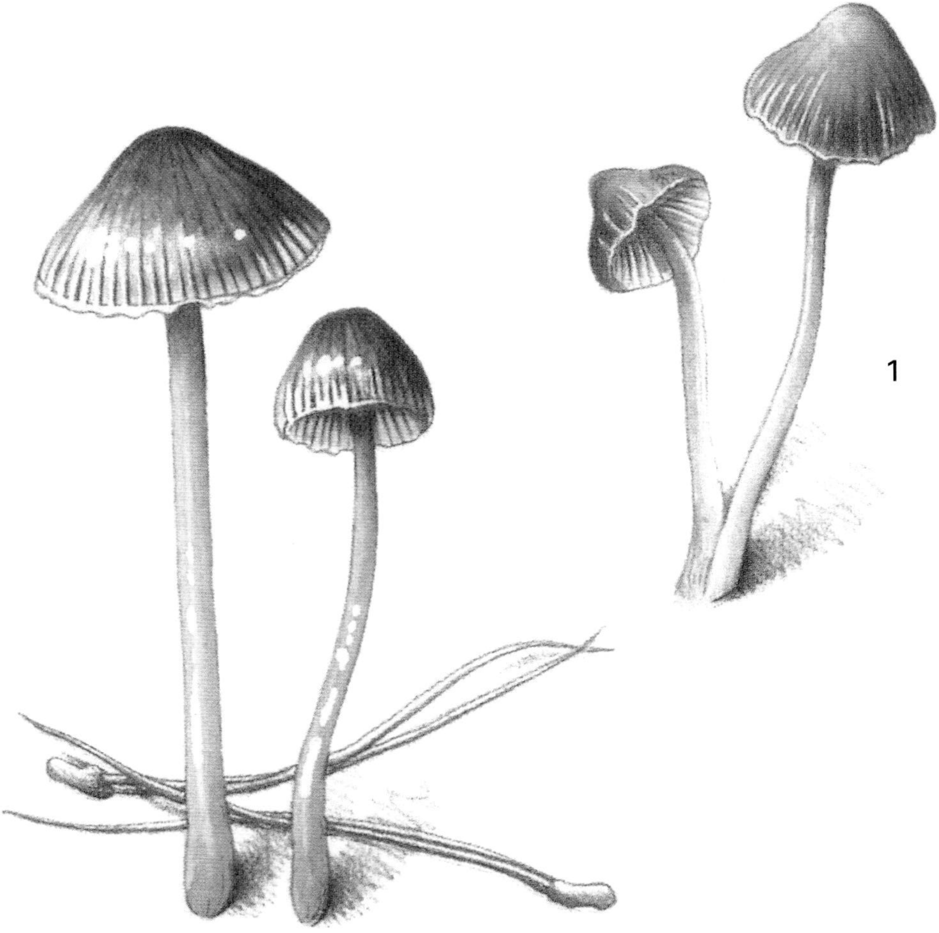

1

The Yellow-stemmed Mycena has delicate slimy stalks and a bell-shaped slimy cap. It is most commonly found under conifers.

Shellfish Russula

Russula xerampelina

Cap 8–15 cm (3¼–6 in); stalk to 7 cm (2¾ in)

Primary Features

Brittle flesh and gills. Cap pinkish purple, blackish in centre. Gills pale ochre, becoming russet. Flesh turns yellow when cut and smells of crab.

Other Features

The very variably coloured cap pales towards the edge, becoming pink or carmine. Gap becomes sunken in centre when mature. Stalk tinged with red, yellowing towards the base. Spore print cream to ochre. Edible.

Habitat and Distribution

Widespread and common under pines, also found under spruce.

Lookalikes

Similarly coloured caps, under conifers: Purple Russula; *R. atrorubens*; *R. turci:* cap with distinct ring of colour around darker centre, under pine and spruce. *R. graveolens:* smells of crab, under broad-leaved trees.

Time of Appearance

August–November

The cap of Shellfish Russula is pinkish purple, and blackish in the centre. The flesh smells of crab, hence its name.

Other Russulas

R. drimeia (**1**): cap 10–15 cm (4–6 in), bright purple violet to wine red, gills bright lemon becoming creamy. Under pine on sandy soils. *R. queletii*, especially under spruce in damp places in mountains, is very similar with a distinctive reddish stalk. **Both inedible**.

Purple Russula *R. amara (caerulea)* (**2**): cap 8–10 cm (3¼–4 in), with a conical outline when young that is unusual for a russula, dark violet to slaty purple. When fully expanded always has an umbo (hump) in centre. Stalk white, gills yellowish. Spore print yellowish. Skin of cap very bitter, making it **inedible**.

R. atrorubens (**3**): cap 6–8 cm (2½–3¼ in), pinkish red at margin, becoming darker purplish in centre. Gills and spore print white. Stalk white. Faint fruity smell. Flesh very acrid. Under conifers, especially in damp places.

1
2
3

Saffron Milk-Cap

Lactarius deliciosus

Cap 10–20 cm (4–8 in); stalk to 5 cm (2 in)

Primary Features

Cap with concentric orange rings on a paler ground, turning green on bruising. Orange gills. Flesh and gills release a sweet orange milk with a slightly peppery aftertaste.

Other Features

A large thickset fungus, becoming vase shaped with age. Cap has slightly frosted or shining surface and a thin inrolled edge. Stalk pale, thick, with orange pits. Flesh off-white. Gills crowded. Spore print white. Edible.

Habitat and Distribution

Widespread and fairly common under pines on neutral or limy soils.

Lookalikes

Red-milk Milk-cap; *L. deterrimus*: cap uniformly pale orange, stalk unpitted, under spruce only; *L. salmonicolor*: orange markings on cap less regular, slightly soapy smell, bitter taste but edible, under firs *(Abies)* only.

Time of Appearance

August–October

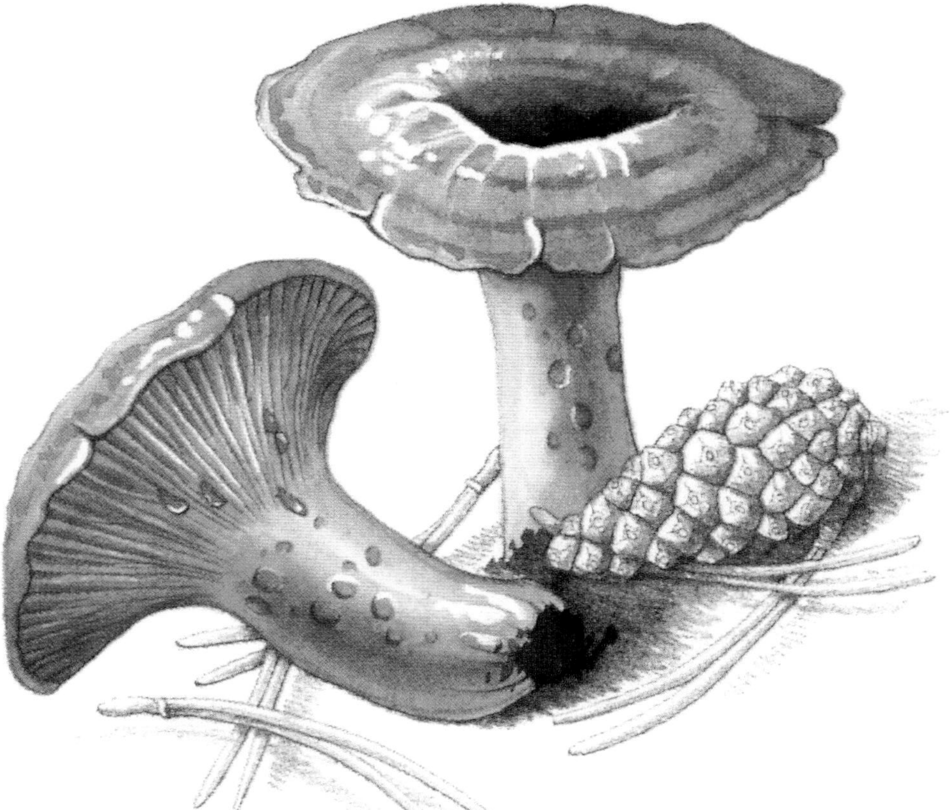

The concentric orange rings and paler orange background on the cap of the Saffron Milk-cap help to distinguish it.

Red-Milk Milk-Cap

Lactarius sanguifluus

Cap 5–10 cm (2–4 in); stalk to 5 cm (2 in)

Primary Features

Pinkish-orange gills release orange milk which immediately turns blood red. Cap dull orange, frosted, with pink and orange zones. Stipe pitted reddish orange.

Other Features

Edible, with a mild taste. Flesh white, immediately reddening when cut. Spore print white. **Red-hot Milk-cap** *(L. rufus)* (**1**) cap 5–10 cm (2–4 in), has a brick-red cap, abundant white milk, cream to yellow arched gills and a very acrid taste.

Habitat and Distribution

Red-milk Milk-cap: (not found in Britain) under pine in southern Europe; Red-hot Milk-cap: common under conifers, also under birch.

Lookalikes

Saffron Milk-cap; *L. deterrimus*: milk turns red slowly; *L. semisanguifluus*: flesh reddens on cutting, then turns green in 24 hours, cap often with a green tinge, stalk not pitted, edible.

Time of Appearance

August–November

1

The Red-milk Milk-cap releases orange milk from its pinkish-orange gills that turns a blood-red colour. It is similar in appearance to the Red-hot Milk-cap.

Curry-Scented Milk-Cap

Cap 2–6 cm ($^{3}/_{4}$–2$^{1}/_{2}$ in); stalk to 5 cm (2 in)

Lactarius camphoratus

Primary Features

Dark chestnut-brown cap, fading to reddish. Strong smell of 'wet linen' when fresh. Flesh and gills release a watery milk. Gills pinkish yellow. Spore print cream.

Other Features

A small slender lactarius. When dried the flesh has a strong spicy smell resembling curry powder and can used as seasoning. The cap often becomes funnel-shaped but retains a small central umbo (hump).

Habitat and Distribution

Quite common and widespread, growing in clusters often at the base of trees, mainly with conifers but also in association with broad-leaved trees.

Lookalikes

Red-hot Milk-cap: generally larger, acrid milk.

Time of Appearance

August–November

Saffron Parasol

Cystoderma amianthinum

Cap 2–5 cm ($^{3}/_{4}$–2 in); stalk to 7 cm (2$^{3}/_{4}$ in)

Primary Features

Yellow cap has a granular surface and remnants of veil around edge. Stalk is covered in granules up to the ring, which points upwards, and is then smooth above. Spore print white.

Other Features

Gills adnate, white to cream. The whitish flesh has a 'mouldy' smell. **Pine Spike-cap** *(Chroogomphus rutilus)* (**1**) has a sticky red-brown cap with a central 'spike', a small ring on the stalk, purplish grey gills and brown spores.

Habitat and Distribution

Saffron Parasol: very common and widespread under conifers, in mixed woods, in grass, and on heaths and moors. Pine Spike-cap: common, especially under pines.

Lookalikes

C. carcharias: paler and greyer in colour, rare, mainly in mountains; *C. granulosum*: red-brown cap and stalk; *Lepiota clypeolaria* and other similar small lepiotas: scaly cap, stalk shaggy below ring, gills free, spore print white.

Time of Appearance

August–October; August–November (**1**)

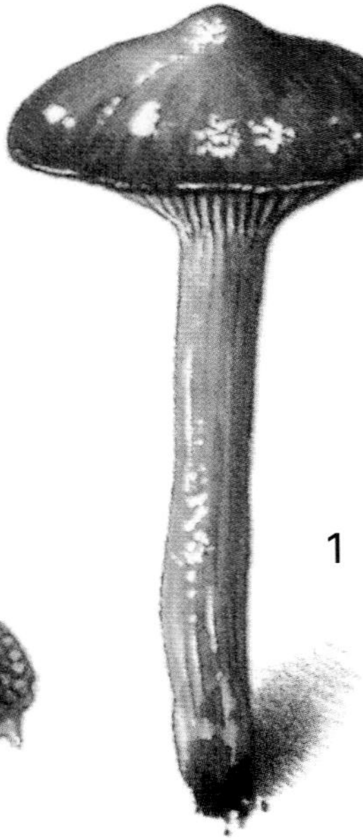
1

Both the cap and the stalk of the Saffron Parasol are very granular to look at. It is a widespread mushroom, found in a variety of habitats.

False Morel

Gyromitra esculenta

Cap 5–10 cm (2–4 in); stalk to 4 cm (1½ in)

Primary Features

Rusty-brown convoluted cap like a brain, set on a short stout paler stalk.

Other Features

The pale brittle flesh has an aromatic smell. **Deadly when raw** and should be avoided. **Cauliflower Mushroom** *(Sparassis crispa)* (**1**) has pale-beige or creamy, flat, curled, ribbon-like divisions. Edible.

Habitat and Distribution

False Morel: under pines, especially in hills, more common in northern Europe. Cauliflower Mushroom: at foot of pines, sometimes on stumps, quite common.

Lookalikes

False Morel: *G. infula*, cap less lobed, stalk longer; **Morel**. Cauliflower Mushroom: *Ramaria* and *Clavulina* spp have coral-like branched fruitbodies and are **inedible**, although not poisonous; **Bear's Head Tooth**.

Time of Appearance

April; August–November (**1**)

1

The cap of the False Morel has the appearance of a brain. It is deadly when raw, despite its aromatic smell. It is found especially in hilly areas.

Chanterelle

Cantharellus cibarius

Cap 3–10 cm (1¼–4 in); stalk to 5 cm (2 in)

Primary Features

Golden-yellow to apricot throughout smelling faintly of apricots. The top-shaped cap soon becomes funnel shaped, and has thick forking ridges on underside instead of true gills.

Other Features

A delicious edible fungus, often found growing in troops. **Funnel Chanterelle** *(C. tubaeformis)* **(1)** has a yellow stalk and forking yellow or greyish ridges on underside of cap, which is grey brown or entirely yellow on top. Good to eat.

Habitat and Distribution

Both the Chanterelle and Funnel Chanterelle are quite common in woods, especially oak and beech, and also under conifers.

Lookalikes

C. lutescens: golden-yellow ridges and stalk, greyish top, delicious; **False Chanterelle**: gills, harmless; **Jack O'Lantern**: on wood, gills, **poisonous**; *Gomphus clavatus*: inverted cone-shaped, ridged outer surface violet.

Time of Appearance

July–December

1

The splendid-looking Chanterelle smells faintly of apricots, as well as being apricot coloured, and tastes delicious.

Wood Hedgehog Mushroom

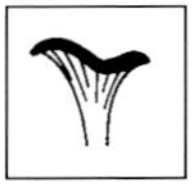

Cap 8–15 cm ($3^1/_4$–6 in); stalk to 6 cm ($2^1/_2$ in)

Hydnum repandum

Primary Features

Fleshy-lobed cap pale fawn or orange-tinged, dark russet in one form, with cream to russet teeth on underside instead of gills. Stalk white, with faint bloom, often misshapen.

Other Features

A good edible fungus with a nutty taste after cooking to remove bitterness. Teeth are brittle, crowded and run down the stalk a little way. The flesh smells faintly of orange-flower water.

Habitat and Distribution

Quite common and widespread under broad-leaved trees and conifers.

Lookalikes

Sarcodon imbricatum: scaly cap, under conifers; *Bankera fuligineoalba*: smaller, less widespread, pinkish-tinged cap, under conifers; *Phellodon niger*: dark blue-grey cap, under conifers; *P. tomentosus:* russet-brown cap, paler at edge.

Time of Appearance

August–November

The Wood Hedgehog Mushroom has 'teeth', rather than gills. It has a slightly bitter taste, which is replaced by a nutty flavour on cooking.

Cep

Boletus edulis

Cap 12–25 cm (4¾–10 in); stalk to 15 cm (6 in)

Primary Features

Date-brown fleshy cap with a greasy surface and white edge. Pores pale, slowly becoming greenish yellow. Upper stalk covered with faint network of white.

Other Features

One of the best-known edible fungi, the most delicious of the boletes, retaining its flavour on drying. The stalk is pale, streaked reddish brown in places. The pores do not change colour on bruising.

Habitat and Distribution

Quite common and widespread under broad-leaved trees, in mixed woods, glades or copses.

Lookalikes

Spring Bolete; **Bay Bolete** and other boletes. Avoid the **Bitter Bolete**. Also avoid boletes with red pores, or dark-brown lobed cap (*B. fragrans*), or with flesh turning blue, some of which are **toxic**.

Time of Appearance

August–November

The Cep is a well known edible fungus, which keeps its flavour once dried. Of the other boletes, those with red pores or blue flesh should be avoided.

Bay Bolete

Xerocomus (Boletus) badius

Cap 8–15 cm (3¼–6 in); stalk to 12 cm (4¾ in)

Primary Features

Cap rich bright brown, pores cream to lemon, bruising greenish when mature, stalk cylindrical rather than swollen at base as in some other boletes.

Other Features

Stalk pale brown streaked with reddish brown. Pale flesh of cap blues slightly to the touch. Edible and good. **Red-capped Bolete** *(Krombholziella aurantiaca)* **(1)** is large and fleshy, with orange-brown cap, pale pores, scaly stork. Edible.

Habitat and Distribution

Bay Bolete: common and widespread under conifers and broad-leaved trees. Golden Bolete: rarer, and found under poplar and birch.

Lookalikes

Red-cracked Bolete and lookalikes; **Brown Birch Bolete**; avoid boletes with pale caps, or red pores or those whose flesh turns blue, some of which are **toxic**.

Time of Appearance

August–November

1

The Bay Bolete is an edible and tasty mushroom. The flesh of the cap turns blue on touching, and bruises turn a greenish colour when mature.

Bluing Bolete

Gyroporus (Boletus) cyanescens Cap 6–15 cm ($2\frac{1}{2}$–6 in); stalk to 10 cm (4 in)

Primary Features

White to pale-ochre cap is smooth and velvety becoming scaly. Pores white to pale ochre, bluing when bruised. Flesh turns instantly blue when broken.

Other Features

An edible bolete despite the bluing flesh. Stalk is white at top, brownish from the base up to an indistinct ring-like zone which soon disappears, and becomes hollow to maturity.

Habitat and Distribution

Quite widespread but not very common, under broad-leaved trees and conifers, especially birch and spruce on sandy soil.

Lookalikes

Chestnut Bolete: chestnut cap, yellowish pores, flesh unchanging, lumpy brown stalk, **possibly toxic**.

Suillus laricini: under larch, olive-grey cap, ring on stalk, flesh greens slightly when cut.

Time of Appearance

July–November

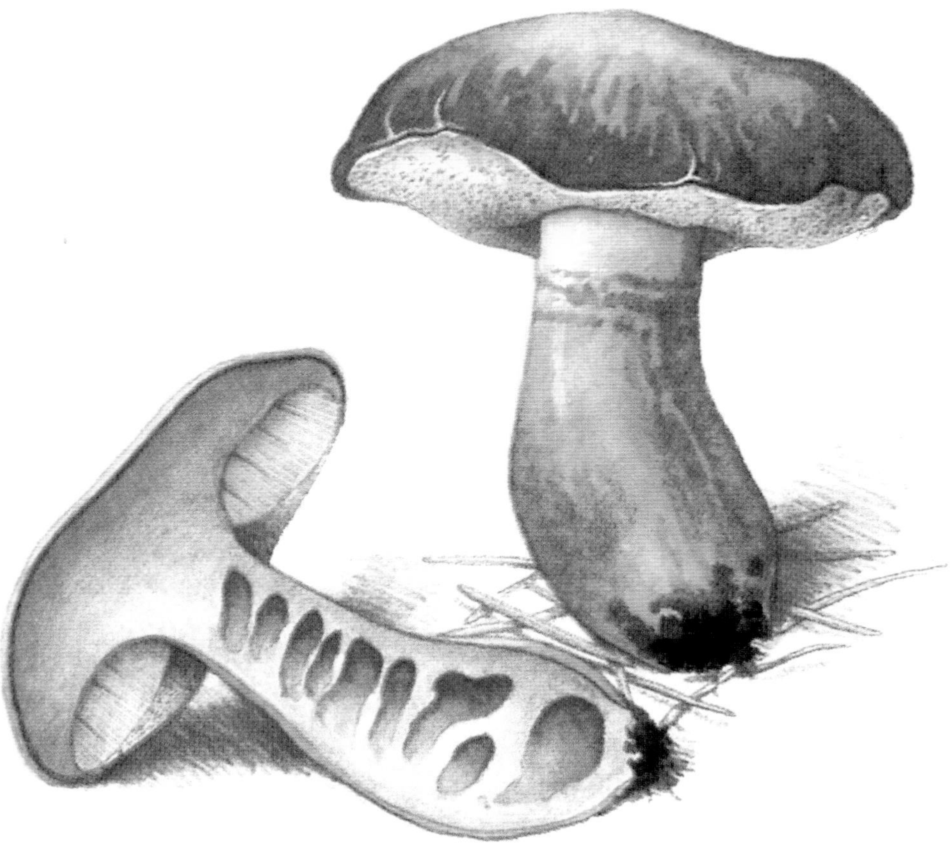

Care should be taken when considering eating any fungi of the bolete family, as they can often be toxic. However, the Bluing Bolete itself is edible.

Bitter Bolete

Tylopilus (Boletus) felleus

Cap 6–15 cm ($2\frac{1}{2}$–6 in); stalk to 12 cm ($4\frac{3}{4}$ in)

Primary Features

Large bolete, with dry grey-brown cap and thick stalk, covered in a darker network. White pores becoming salmon pink when older.

Other Features

The very bitter flesh makes this bolete **inedible**, although not toxic, and can spoil a dish of ceps if even one is included in error.

Habitat and Distribution

In both broad-leaved and coniferous woods, common locally but not widespread throughout Europe.

Lookalikes

Cep; **Spring Bolete**; **Bay Bolete** and other **boletes**.

Time of Appearance

June–November

The Bitter Bolete is not toxic, but the taste is so unpleasantly bitter that it is inedible.

Old Man of the Woods

Cap 10–20 cm (4–8 in); stalk to 12 cm ($4\frac{3}{4}$ in)

Strobilomyces strobilaceus (floccopus)

Primary Features

Cap covered with thick grey-brown to black scales when young, resembling an immature pine cone. Stalk with a shaggy ring, becoming indistinct in older specimens. Spores purple brown.

Other Features

This unusual bolete has whitish pores covered with a veil when young, later becoming greyish. Flesh reddens on bruising. **Inedible**.

Habitat and Distribution

Uncommon, often found under beech, and also with conifers.

Lookalikes

Unlikely to be confused with any other bolete. Its purple spores are an unambiguous distinguishing factor, other boletes having whitish spores.

Time of Appearance

September–November

Russet Shank

Collybia dryophila

Cap 2–5 cm ($^3/_4$–2 in); stalk to 5 cm (2 in)

Primary Features

Smooth bright red-brown cap becoming yellow with age. Crowded white gills, adnexed. Bright orange-brown stalk, paler at top, smooth. Spore print white.

Other Features

Slightly poisonous when raw, so do not eat. **Wood Woolly-foot** *(C. peronata)* (**1**) has a leathery yellowish-brown cap and stalk, which is woolly at the foot. Bruised flesh smells of vinegar. White spores. Not toxic but not edible.

Habitat and Distribution

Common and widespread, Russet Shank especially under oak and beech, and on heaths, amongst bracken, Wood Woolly-foot in woods of all kinds.

Lookalikes

Collybias have yellowish, white or brown caps, tough stalks, gills adnate to free, spores white or pinkish. *C. confluens*: pinkish downy stalk; **Spindle Shank**: in clusters under beech or oak, brown cap, greyish gills, swollen stalk tapers at base.

Time of Appearance

July–November; September–November (**1**)

1

The Russet Shank is found throughout summer and autumn, especially under oak and beech trees. Although non-toxic, it is not edible.

Lilac Mycena

Mycena pura

Cap 3–5 cm ($1\frac{1}{4}$–2 in); stalk to 6 cm ($2\frac{1}{2}$ in)

Primary Features

Small fleshy rose-pink to lilac mushroom with white to pinkish gills. Smells of radishes. Fribrous stalk.

Other Features

One of the more robust mycenas, the bell-shaped cap at first becoming convex to flat, sometimes with a central knob. Edge is striated. Gills adnate, spaced quite far apart with short gills in between at cap edge. Spore print white.

Habitat and Distribution

Common and widespread, occurring in woods of all kinds, especially beech and oak, but also under various conifers.

Lookalikes

M. pelianthina: dark edge to gill; **Milk-drop Mycena**; mycenas have fragile bell-shaped caps in various colours, tough stalks, adnexed/adnate to sinuate gills, white or pink spore prints; **Amethyst Deceiver**: thick violet gills.

Time of Appearance

June–December

This small rose-pink mushroom, the Lilac Mycena, smells of radishes. Its bell-shaped cap becomes convex or flat as it ages.

Milk-Drop Mycena

Mycena galopus

Cap 0.5–3 cm ($\frac{1}{4}$–$1\frac{1}{4}$ in); stalk to 4 cm ($1\frac{1}{2}$ in)

Primary Features

Small greyish-brown fragile mushroom, with a hemispherical cap striated at edge. Stalk exudes white milky fluid when broken. Gills white, spore print white.

Other Features

Cap colour can vary from whitish to almost black. Gills annexed. The slender fibrous stalk is smooth with minute hairs at the base, resembling a root.

Habitat and Distribution

Common and widespread, found growing amongst leaf litter in all kinds of woods, never on living trees.

Lookalikes

One of numerous small brown mycenas, this can be distinguished from most of them by its white milk.

M. metata: pale pinkish-brown cap, no milk, smells of iodoform;

M. filopes: no milk, smell of iodoform, usually in moss.

Time of Appearance

July–December

The Milk-drop Mycena has a minute cap, which can be as small as 0.5 cm ($^1/_4$ in). It can be found amongst the leaf litter of the woodland floor.

Common White Inocybe

Cap 1–3 cm ($\frac{1}{2}$–1$\frac{1}{4}$ in); stalk to 5 cm (2 in)

Inocybe geophylla

Primary Features

Cap and stalk white and silky, stalk powdery at apex only. Gills crowded, yellowish to clay brown, adnexed. Spore print brown.

Other Features

One of a number of **very poisonous** small white mushrooms. Cap colour can vary from white to lilac with a pale-ochre tinge in centre.

Habitat and Distribution

Common and widespread in all kinds of woods, often growing in damp soil by paths.

Lookalikes

Inocybes often have conical caps (e.g. **Deadly Inocybe**), or flatter caps with a central knob, often radially streaked and splitting at edge. Most are some shade of brown. Gills and spores brown.

All should be avoided, many are toxic.

Time of Appearance

June–November

Brown Roll-Rim

Paxillus involutus

Cap 5–25 cm (2–10 in); stalk to 7 cm (2¾ in)

Primary Features

Cap olive brown to rusty brown, felty, sticky when wet, with inrolled rim. Gills easily separable from cap, cream to dirty yellow brown, crowded, running down stem. Spores dull brown.

Other Features

A robust fungus which could at first sight be confused with some lactarias but is not milky. Gills spotted rust brown. Stalk pale brown, thick and smooth. **Not to be eaten** as it can have a cumulative toxic effect.

Habitat and Distribution

Very common in mixed woods, often found under birch and oak.

Lookalikes

P. atrotomentosus: velvety-black stalk, on conifer stumps; *Gomphidius glutinosus*: sticky grey-brown cap, whitish stalk with a constriction and ring-like zone immediately beneath gills, under conifers.

Time of Appearance

August–November

The Brown Roll-rim is poisonous, but it is not one of the most dangerous species. The cap feels sticky when wet and has an inrolled rim.

The Sickener

Russula emetica

Cap 3–10 cm (1¼–4 in); stalk to 7 cm (2¾ in)

Primary Features

Brittle gills and flesh, pure scarlet or cherry-red shiny cap, white gills and stalk. Skin of cap peels completely to show white or faintly reddish flesh. Very acrid taste.

Other Features

One of numerous bright red-capped russulas, this can cause vomiting in the raw state and **should be avoided**. The flesh has a distinctive smell of coconut. Gills adnate, quite widely spaced. Spore print white.

Habitat and Distribution

Common and widespread under both conifers and broad-leaved trees.

Lookalikes

The red-capped, white-spored russulas are difficult to distinguish from each other and are **all best avoided**.

Some red-capped russulas have cream gills, ochre to yellow spore print and a mild taste. None is worth eating.

Time of Appearance

July–October

The Sickener can cause vomiting if eaten when raw. Despite its distinctive coconut smell it has a very acrid taste and really is not worth even trying.

Blackening Russula

Russula nigricans

Cap 10–20 cm (4–8 in); stalk to 7 cm (2¾ in)

Primary Features

Brittle gills and flesh. Whitish to grey-brown cap and stalk both turn black with age. Flesh reddens (blackens in old caps) on cutting. Gills thick, whitish, with short gills in between.

Other Features

The large blackened caps persist for a long time. Spores white. Edible but not worth eating. **Foetid Russula** *(R. foetens)* (**1**), cap 12–20 cm (4¾–8 in), has a dirty yellow-grey slimy cap and a sickening smell. Gills whitish, spores pale cream.

Habitat and Distribution

Both are common in mixed woods, especially broad-leaved woods.

Lookalikes

Blackening Russula: *R. albonigra*, rarer, gills crowded, flesh blackens without reddening; *R. delica*, remains white to pale brownish; *R. densifolia*, crowded gills. Foetid Russula: *R. laurocerasi*, smells of marzipan.

Time of Appearance

June/July–October/November

1

The caps of Blackening Russula are quite large (up to 20 cm/8 in). The flesh blackens as it ages, but starts off whitish to grey brown.

Common Yellow Russula

Cap 8–12 cm ($3\frac{1}{4}$–$4\frac{3}{4}$ in); stalk to 7 cm ($2\frac{3}{4}$ in)

Russula ochroleuca

Primary Features

Golden-yellow cap, becoming sunken in centre. Gills white, stalk greyish. Taste variable, from peppery to mild. Spore print pale cream.

Other Features

Cap often tinged with ochre, orange or green. **Grey-blue Russula** *(R. parazurea)* **(1)** has a distinctive matt blue-grey cap with a slight bloom towards the edge. Gills and spore print cream. Edible.

Habitat and Distribution

Common Yellow Russula: very common and widespread; Grey-blue Russula: common, typically found in oak and beech woods.

Lookalikes

Common Yellow Russula: *R. fellea*, straw coloured, beech and oak woods; *R. claroflava*: brighter yellow, yellow gills, under birch; Grey-blue Russula: *R. ionochlora*, grey cap with greenish or violet tints, under beech.

Time of Appearance

August–November

1

The golden yellow cap of the Common Yellow Russula can be tinged with ochre, orange or green. It is edible and the taste varies from mild to peppery.

Dirty Milk-Cap

Lactarius plumbeus (turpis) Cap 5–12 cm (2–4¾ in); stalk to 6 cm (2½ in)

Primary Features

Flesh and gills release white acrid milk when broken. Slightly slimy olive-brown to blackish cap, rolled under at edge. Yellowish gills, bruising brown. Stem grey brown.

Other Features

Large squat fleshy mushroom, cap edge slightly velvety when young. Gills crowded, running down stem a short way, soon becoming spotted with grey. Stalk stout and tapering to base. Spore print cream. **Inedible**.

Habitat and Distribution

Common and widespread in damp soil under birch, also under pine.

Lookalikes

Slimy Milk-cap: concentric rings of spots on cap, under beech; *L. fluens*: white stalk, under beech; **Brown Roll-rim**: not milky.

Time of Appearance

July–November

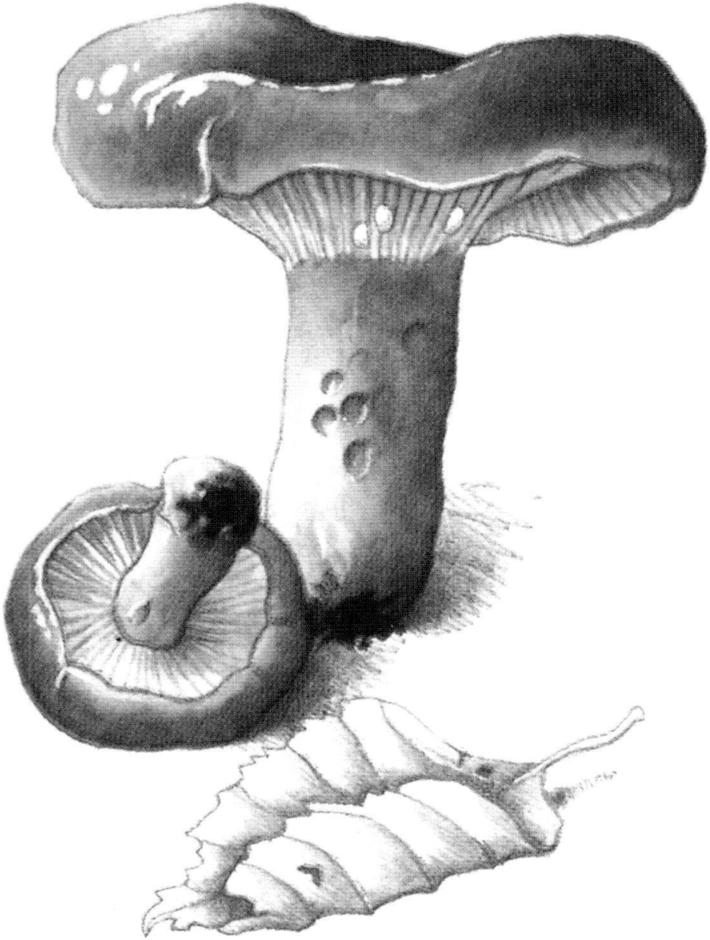

Amethyst Deceiver

Laccaria amethystea

Cap 1–8 cm ($\frac{1}{2}$–$3\frac{1}{4}$ in); stalk to 10 cm (4 in)

Primary Features

Vivid violet throughout when young, fading bluish or whitish with age. Gills thick, far apart, adnate to decurrent. Spore print white.

Other Features

The cap has a matt surface covered with fine scales and soon flattens out. Stem fibrous, usually curved. Harmless but not worth eating.

Habitat and Distribution

Very common everywhere in shady woods and damp places.

Lookalikes

Lilac Mycena; Deceiver.

Time of Appearance

August–November

The Amethyst Deceiver keeps its violet colour when young, but fades to blue or white as it ages. Not to be confused with the Lilac Mycena or the Deceiver.

Spotted Collybia

Collybia maculata

Cap 5–10 cm (2–4 in); stalk to 12 cm ($4^{3}/_{4}$ in)

Primary Features

Smooth white cap with rusty-pink spots. Crowded white gills, adnate or nearly free. Fibrous white stalk, sometimes with reddish stripes. Pale pinkish-buff spore sprint.

Other Features

Bitter and indigestible, should not be eaten. **Broad-gilled Agaric** *(Megacollybia platyphylla)* (**1**) cap 6–15 cm ($2^{1}/_{2}$–6 in) is a translucent grey brown, streaked with dark fibrils. The white stalk ends in 'roots'. Spores white. Not worth eating.

Habitat and Distribution

Common and widespread, Spotted Collybia mainly under birch or conifers, and on heaths and moors; Broad-gilled Agaric in leaf litter and decaying wood of beech, oak, more rarely conifers.

Lookalikes

Cloudy Agaric; **Sweating Mushroom**: smaller, decurrent gills, white spore print, **poisonous**; other collybias have reddish, brown, white or yellowish caps, tough stalks and adnate to free gills, spore print white or pinkish.

Time of Appearance

July–November; September–November (**1**)

1

This indigestible mushroom should not be eaten. The Spotted Collybia has a bitter taste. It is found under birch or conifer trees, and on heaths and moors.

Cloudy Agaric

Clitocybe nebularis

Cap 12–20 cm (4¾–8 in); stalk to 10 cm (4 in)

Primary Features

Fleshy cap convex, becoming flatter with central umbo. Yellowish-grey cap and stalk, gills thin, crowded, cream to yellowish, slightly decurrent. Spore print white.

Other Features

Do not eat as it disagrees with some people and can also be confused with poisonous species. **Club-footed Clitocybe** *(C. clavipes)* **(1)** has a club-shaped downy base to stalk, and watery flesh smelling of bitter almonds. Not worth eating.

Habitat and Distribution

Common and widespread in both coniferous woods and under broad-leaved trees.

Lookalikes

Other larger clitocybes: *C. geotropa*, smells of new-mown hay; *C. inornata*: pale coffee-coloured cap, smell becomes unpleasantly fishy. Clitocybes are fleshy, white spored, with decurrent to adnate gills and white, brown or greyish caps.

Time of Appearance

August/September–December

1

Short Rhodocybe

Rhodocybe truncata

Cap 4–12 cm ($1\frac{1}{2}$–$4\frac{3}{4}$ in); stalk to 8 cm ($3\frac{1}{4}$ in)

Primary Features

Fleshy pale pinkish-brown to russet cap with irregular inrolled edge. Gills decurrent, cream to similar colour as cap. Spore print pink.

Other Features

The cap has a felty surface. Gills are crowded, forked and narrow. The stem is thick and solid, whitish tinted pink. Edible.

Habitat and Distribution

In mixed woods and grassy thickets, often growing in clusters or rings.

Lookalikes

Poison Pie: **toxic**, and other *Hebeloma* spp, **none of which should be eaten**, brownish spore print; **entolomas**, some of which are **deadly**, also have pink spore prints; **The Miller**.

Time of Appearance

September–November

Wood Blewit

Lepista (Clitocybe) nuda

Cap 10–15 cm (4–6 in); stalk to 10 cm (4 in)

Primary Features

Distinctive large smooth bluish-lilac cap when young, becoming tan. Gills sinuate, lilac becoming yellowish, and can be separated easily from cap. Spore print pinkish buff.

Other Features

This common mushroom is good to eat after cooking (although some people are allergic to it) but is **slightly poisonous when raw**. Stalk stout, fibrous, lilac. The flesh is thick, firm and white with a lilac tinge.

Habitat and Distribution

Common and widespread in open woods, along paths, in gardens, often growing in groups.

Lookalikes

Blewit (*L. saeva*): buff cap, pinkish-beige gills, lilac stalk, in grass and wood edges, edible. Make sure you do not have **Lead Poisoner** or a **clitocybe**, which also have pinkish spore prints, or a **tricholoma** (white spores).

Time of Appearance

September–December

Although some people are allergic to the Wood Blewit it does taste good once cooked. Cooking is important as it is slightly poisonous when raw.

Poison Pie

Hebeloma crustuliniforme

Cap 5–10 cm (2–4 in); stalk to 8 cm (3¼ in)

Primary Features

Sticky cream to russet cap with paler margin. Gills crowded, pale brownish grey to cinnamon brown, edged with water droplets when young. Spore print brown to rust.

Other Features

Poisonous. This mushroom smells of radishes when young, has a bitter taste and **can cause severe gastric upsets**. The stout cylindrical stalk is white, flaky, with white granules on surface towards apex.

Habitat and Distribution

Quite common and widespread in deciduous and mixed woods and in grass, sometimes forming fairy rings.

Lookalikes

Hebelomas have fine-toothed gill edges (visible under a hand lens) and brown spores, and usually sticky caps in shades of brown. **All are poisonous**. **Tricholomas**: white spores, **entolomas**: pink spores.

Time of Appearance

August–November

Tricholomas

Marvellous Tricholoma *(T. portentosum)* (**1**): cap 10–15 cm (4–6 in), grey brown, slightly conical, tinged yellowish, with dark fibrils radiating out from blackish centre. Sinuate gills and stalk white, tinged lemon. Spore print white. An excellent edible mushroom with a floury smell.

White Tricholoma *(T. columbetta)* (**2**): has a satiny-white surface to cap, sticky when damp, and white sinuate gills and stalk, cap and stalk discolouring with blue or pink spots. White spores. Under beech or birch. Edible.

Leopard Tricholoma *(T. pardinum)* (**3**): cap 15–25 cm (6–10 in), large mushroom with a fleshy cap incurved at edges, covered with brownish scales on a paler ground. Stout smooth pale stem. Gills whitish. Earthy smell becoming unpleasant. Spore print white. **Highly poisonous**. Not found in Britain. Mainly in beech and fir woods.

3
1
2

False Chanterelle

Hygrophoropsis aurantiaca Cap 3–6 cm (1¼–2½ in); stalk to 4 cm (1½ in)

Primary Features

Bright golden-yellow to orange fungus, cap soon sunken in centre. Gills forked, bright orange, running down stalk. No distinctive smell. Spore print white to cream.

Other Features

This harmless Chanterelle lookalike is edible but not really worth eating. The surface of the cap is matt, dry and sometimes downy, and eventually becomes brownish. The flesh is yellowish and rather tough.

Habitat and Distribution

Common and widespread, often occurring in large troops, under both coniferous and broad-leaved trees.

Lookalikes

Chanterelle; Jack O'Lantern: **poisonous**, grows on wood.

Time of Appearance

August–November

The False Chanterelle looks similar to the Chanterelle, but it has an unremarkable taste. Must not be confused with the Jack O'Lantern, which is poisonous.

Purple Cortinarius

Cortinarius purpurascens

Cap 10–15 cm (4–6 in); stalk to 10 cm (4 in)

Primary Features

Brown ring-like remnants of veil on stalk. Slimy cap is reddish brown to greeny greyish, violet at edges. Gills lilac, becoming rusty with age. Spore print rust brown.

Other Features

Large fleshy mushroom in which edge of cap is joined to stalk by a fine veil when young. The stout pale-violet stem has a bulbous base with a distinct rim. Harmless but **inedible**. Take care not to mistake it for the edible Wood Blewit.

Habitat and Distribution

Widespread but not abundant, in clumps, in coniferous and mixed woods.

Lookalikes

C. alboviolaceus: pale silky cap, lilac gills, under beech, oak; *C. violaceus* (**1**): (not found in Britain) deep-violet cap, gills and stalk; *C. speciosissimus*: conical brown cap, brown stem and gills, **deadly**, coniferous woods, moors.

Time of Appearance

September–November

1

Red-Gilled Cortinarius

Cortinarius semisanguineus

Cap 5–8 cm (2–3¼ in); stalk to 7 cm (2¾ in)

Primary Features

Reddish-brown ring-like remnants of veil on stalk. Cap velvety, pale yellowish brown to olive brown, with a central knob. Blood-red crowded adnate gills. Spore print brown.

Other Features

One of several cortinarias with red gills. Edge of cap attached to stalk by a fine veil when young. Stalk yellowish. Flesh pale, yellowish, smelling faintly of radishes. Not edible and **may be toxic**.

Habitat and Distribution

Quite common and widespread in coniferous and birch woods, and on heaths, often growing in clusters.

Lookalikes

C. sanguineus: blood-red cap, gills and flesh, common; *C. cinnabarinus*: similar, more orange-red, rarer, under beech, hornbeam; *C. orellanus*: **deadly**, orange to rusty-brown gills, orange-brown cap, in warm places.

Time of Appearance

August–November

Green Stropharia

Stropharia aeruginosa

Cap 5–8 cm (2–3¼ in); stalk to 6 cm (2½ in)

Primary Features

Slimy cap is a bright bluish green when young, becoming yellowish with age, and has white fleecy scales at the edge. The stalk has a greyish ring. Gills adnate, violet grey.

Other Features

The slimy stalk is smooth above the ring, fleecy or covered with white flecks below, and paler than the cap. The vivid colour of the cap soon fades, and the gills become chocolate brown. Spore print purplish brown. **Inedible**.

Habitat and Distribution

Quite common and widespread in grassy woods and copses, gardens and pastures.

Lookalikes

Other stropharias have beige or brown caps, whitish stalks with a ring, purple-brown spores, greyish-violet adnate or slightly decurrent gills. The very common *S. semiglobata* with a yellowish hemispherical cap grows on dung.

Time of Appearance

June–November

The slimy blue-green cap of the Green Stropharia has white fleecy scales around the edge. As it ages the cap yellows and the gills become chocolate brown.

The Gypsy

Rozites caperata

Cap 8–12 cm ($3\frac{1}{4}$–$4\frac{3}{4}$ in); stalk to 10 cm (4 in)

Primary Features

Pale golden to dull ochre-yellow cap sometimes with silvery veil covering centre. Gills pale becoming clay brown, edges finely toothed (under a hand lens). Whitish ring on stalk.

Other Features

Pale-brown spores. Stalk pale, striated, ring fleshy and remaining on stalk for a long time. Gills adnate, thick and crowded. Very good to eat if mushrooms undamaged by insects can be found.

Habitat and Distribution

Fairly common under birch and pine in mountainous woods on acid soil in northern Europe.

Lookalikes

Poison Pie and other *Hebeloma* spp: no ring or very indistinct ring-like remains of veil on stalk.

Time of Appearance

August–December

The Gypsy is very tasty to eat, but unfortunately insects often get there first. Look for the Gypsy in the mountainous woods of northern Europe.

The Prince

Agaricus augustus

Cap 10–25 cm (4–10 in); stalk to 20 cm (8 in)

Primary Features

A large agaric, the cap covered with small golden to dark-brown scales. Stalk bruises yellow. Ring large and hanging. Flesh discolours brownish, smells of bitter almonds.

Other Features

A good edible mushroom. The young cap is hemispherical, expanding flat with age. Stalk is scaly below ring. Greyish to dark-brown gills very crowded. Spore print dark brown.

Habitat and Distribution

Quite common under various broad-leaved trees and conifers.

Lookalikes

Yellow-staining Mushroom: white silky cap, stains yellow at base of stalk, **toxic**; *A. silvicola*: white cap, stains yellow where bruised, in mixed or broad-leaved woods, edible; most other mushrooms are found in open grassland.

Time of Appearance

July–October

The Prince has a cap covered with small golden-brown or dark-brown scales. Although its flesh smells of bitter almonds, it is a good edible mushroom.

Fly Agaric

Amanita muscaria

Cap 10–20 cm (4–8 in); stalk to 15 cm (6 in)

Primary Features

Unmistakable bright-red cap covered with small white patches of the universal veil. White gills and spores. White stalk with ring. Volva only a series of ridges at base of stalk.

Other Features

A familiar mushroom in northern Europe, illustrated in countless fairy-tales. Young fruitbodies are entirely covered in a white veil. The white patches may become washed off in older specimens and caps fade orange red. **Poisonous**.

Habitat and Distribution

Very common under birch or pine on poor soils.

Lookalikes

The edible and good **Caesar's Mushroom** (not found in Britain) has a smooth red cap with no or larger remnant of white veil, yellow stalk and gills, and a large sac-like white volva, and has a more southerly distribution.

Time of Appearance

August–November

With the traditional fairytale white-spotted red cap, the Fly Agaric seems a familiar sight. It is found commonly in northern Europe.

The Blusher

Amanita rubescens

Cap 10–18 cm (4–7¼ in); stalk to 10 cm (4 in)

Primary Features

Light-brown cap covered with small dingy-yellowish patches of veil. Gills and spores white. Stalk white flushed pink with hanging ring. No apparent volva. Flesh white, flushing pink.

Other Features

This is one of the few edible and excellent amanitas, but must be cooked as it is **indigestible when raw**. Gills are speckled pink in older specimens. **Do not confuse with the Panther**.

Habitat and Distribution

Common and widespread under all kinds of trees.

Lookalikes

The Panther: **deadly poisonous**, white scales on cap, basal bulb with remains of volva, flesh does not turn pink;

A. spissa: dark-brown cap with greyish scales, flesh does not turn pink, not poisonous but not worth eating.

Time of Appearance

July–November

The Blusher is not a poisonous species, but it is indigestible if even slightly uncooked. However, must not be confused with the Panther, which is deadly.

Lemon Amanita

Amanita citrina

Cap 6–10 cm ($2\frac{1}{2}$–4 in); stalk to 12 cm ($4\frac{3}{4}$ in)

Primary Features

Pale lemon-yellow cap, sometimes almost white, with loose patches of the white veil adhering to it. Margin not striated. Bulbous base with volva. White ring on stalk.

Other Features

This amanita is not poisonous but **should not be collected for eating** for fear of confusion with the Death Cap. It smells of raw potatoes and has an unpleasant taste. Gills and spore print white.

Habitat and Distribution

Widespread and quite common, under broad-leaved trees and conifers. Also found on heaths.

Lookalikes

Other amanitas, especially **Death Cap** and **Jonquil Amanita**.

Time of Appearance

August–October

Fluted Black Helvella

Cap 3–5 cm ($1\frac{1}{4}$–2 in); stalk to 6 cm ($2\frac{1}{2}$ in)

Helvella lacunosa

Primary Features

Dark-grey thin saddle-shaped cap, with wavy lobes, and with no gills, pores or ridges on underside. The hollow paler-grey stalk is deeply fluted and furrowed.

Other Features

A distinctive fungus with upper surface of cap sometimes slightly wrinkled, lower surface slightly paler and smooth. Eaten in some countries but **not recommended** as related fungi are known to contain toxins.

Habitat and Distribution

Quite common and widespread in coniferous and broad-leaved woods, especially on burnt soil.

Lookalikes

Leptopodia atra: smaller, with a round lobed cap and slender blackish stalk; **Fluted White Helvella**: whitish to beige cap, fluted white stalk; **Common Morel**: rounded cap with honeycombed surface.

Time of Appearance

September–October

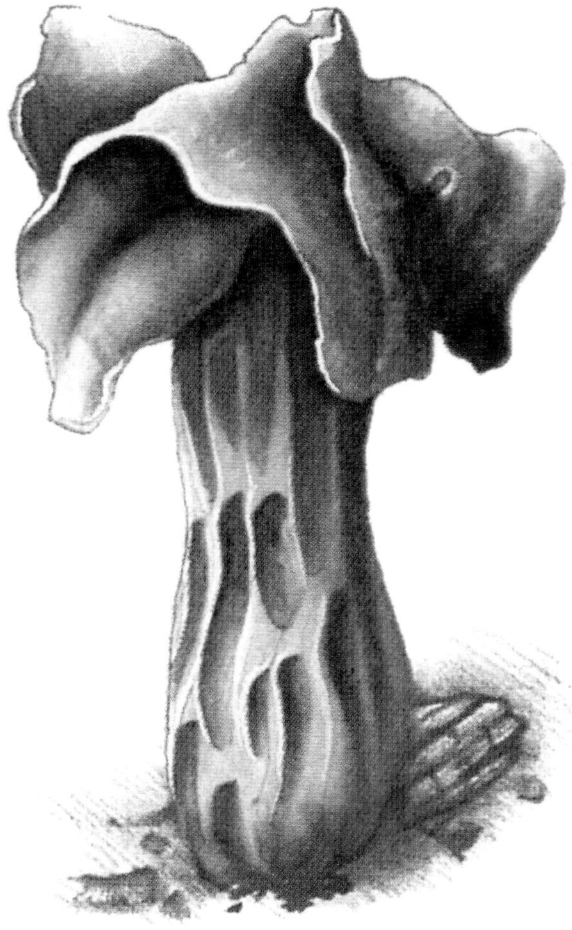

The Fluted Black Helvella has a deeply fluted stalk and a wavy, and sometimes, wrinkled, cap. It is not recommended for eating.

Stinkhorn

Phallus impudicus

'Cap' 3–4 cm (1¼–1½ in); height up to 20 cm (8 in)

Primary Features

Unmistakable, recognizable by its shape and strong offensive smell. The stout spongy white stalk carries a slimy foetid green-black mass of spores at its top.

Other Features

Often first detected by the unpleasant smell. The slime and spores are eventually eaten by flies, exposing the pitted surface of the cap. The immature fruitbody is like an 'egg', its remnants forming a volva-like sac at stalk base.

Habitat and Distribution

Common and widespread in woods and gardens, especially on rich soil.

Lookalikes

P. hadriani: similar, much rarer, on dunes by the sea, spore mass has faint sweetish smell when still in the 'egg'; *Mutinus caninus*: similar shape and structure, much smaller, stalk yellowish, spores borne direct on tip of stalk.

Time of Appearance

July–November

The Stinkhorn does indeed have an unpleasant smell, which, in addition to the small, pitted cap, help to distinguish it from other species.

Common Earthball

Scleroderma citrinum

Fruitbody 6–12 cm ($2\frac{1}{2}$–$4\frac{3}{4}$ in) diameter

Primary Features

Hard ball-like fungus growing directly on the ground, with a dirty-yellowish scaly outer covering, becoming cracked, and a powdery purplish spore mass inside.

Other Features

This very common earthball has no stalk and 'roots' directly into the ground. The internal mass of spores is initially pinkish, eventually turns purple and escapes through cracks in the thick hard outer wall.

Habitat and Distribution

Very common in woods, parks and heaths, especially on mossy peaty ground and under birches.

Lookalikes

S. bovista: thinner, smooth outer wall, short stalk-like base very earthy, less common; *S. areolatum* and *S. verrucosum*: surface more finely scaled, base has a short tapering stalk, spore mass olive brown, common.

Time of Appearance

August–December

The Common Earthball grows directly out of the ground, having no stalk. The internal spores are initially pink, but turn purple with age.

Earthstar

Geastrum triplex

Fruitbody 8–12 cm (3¼–4¾ in) diameter

Primary Features

Yellowish grey-brown sac containing spores sits in a saucer supported on curved-back segments of fruitbody outer wall, which has split radially.

Other Features

In this earthstar, the rays are rather fleshy and cracked across. It also has a distinct halo around the small opening in the inner sac through which the spores are released.

Habitat and Distribution

Quite common and widespread in woods.

Lookalikes

G. sessile: rays not cracked across, no saucer at base of inner sac; *G. fornicatum*: rays form a four-legged support 5–10 cm (2–4 in) high, rare; *G. quadrifidum*: similar to latter but smaller; *Astraeus hygrometricus*: rays spread out.

Time of Appearance

August–October

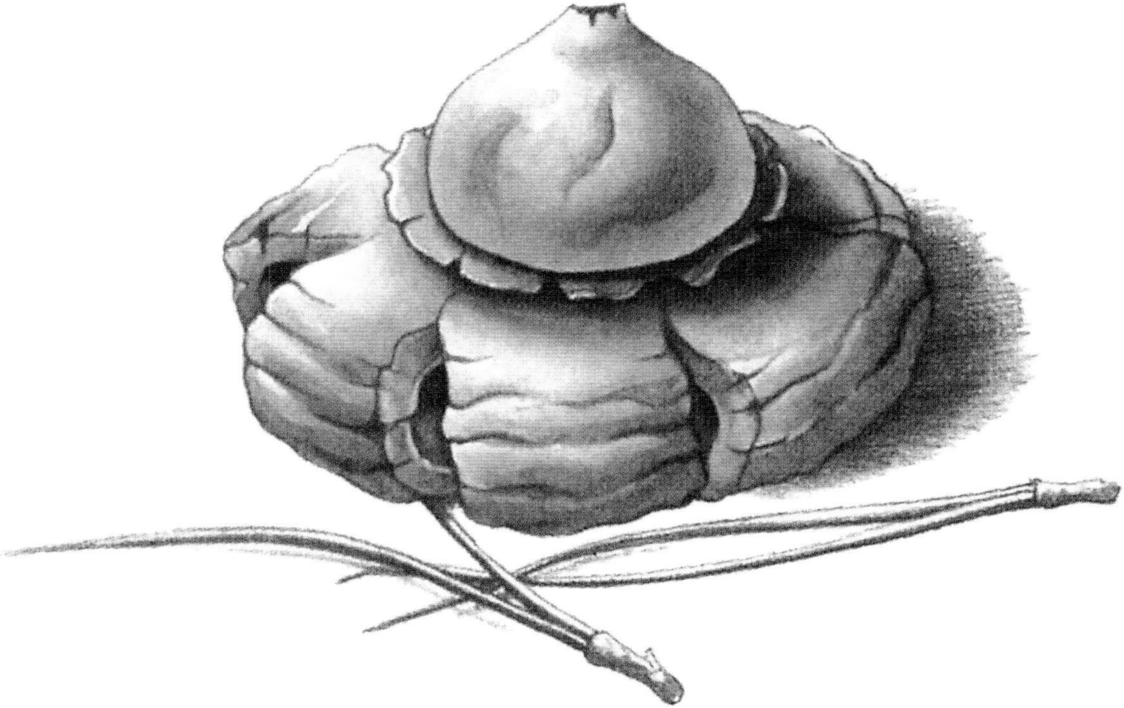

The Earthstar has a rather fleshy, but cracked, appearance. The spores are released from the 'halo' around the small opening in the inner sac.

Crested Coral

Clavulina cristata

Fruitbody 3–10 cm ($1\frac{1}{4}$–4 in) across

Primary Features

White coral-like fruitbody, branching, with expanded toothed tips to branches. Flesh white.

Other Features

One of a type of fungus commonly called Fairy Clubs or Coral Fungi. Some related species have thick unbranched club-like fruitbodies. The Crested Coral is edible, but some other species are not.

Habitat and Distribution

Common on the ground in woods of all kinds, related species also occur in grass or grow directly on wood.

Lookalikes

C. cinerea: ash grey but otherwise very similar; *Ramaria* spp: generally more massive, lilac, yellow, pale pink or olive, not pure white; *Clavulinopsis corniculata*: yellow, tips of branches pointed, not toothed.

Time of Appearance

June–July

The Crested Coral is commonly found in woodlands and also amongst grass. It has several lookalike species, but they vary in colour.

Hygrocybes (Wax Agarics)

Small colourful (yellow, red, orange, pink) mushrooms which grow in grass, appearing in late summer and autumn. All have rather thick 'waxy' gills and white spores.

Parrot Mushroom *(Hygrocybe psittacina)* (**1**): cap 2–5 cm ($^{3}/_{4}$–2 in), sticky, shades of brownish yellow tinged greenish and/or reddish. Stalk tough, slimy, green at apex. Gills adnate, yellowish. Heaths, pasture, grassy woods. *H. ceracea* is waxy yellow, cap sticky, gills decurrent. *H. punicea* is much larger, cap 5–12 cm (2–4$^{3}/_{4}$ in), blunt topped blood red, sticky when damp. Gills adnexed, yellow tinted red.

Orange Waxy Cap *(H. miniata)* (2): cap 1–2 cm ($^{1}/_{2}$–$^{3}/_{4}$ in), scarlet or orange red, not slimy, with small scales in centre. Gills adnate decurrent, orange with yellow edges. Likes damp places. *H. coccinea* has a blood-red bell-shaped cap, yellow gills.

Conical Slimy Cap *(H. conica)* (**3**): cap 1–4 cm ($^{1}/_{2}$–1$^{1}/_{2}$ in), orange red, blackening. Gills yellowish, free. Heaths, pasture, grassy woods. *H. nigrescens*, also blackening, larger, white base to stalk.

3
2
1

Liberty Cap

Psilocybe semilanceata

Cap 0.5–1 cm ($\frac{1}{4}$–$\frac{1}{2}$ in); stalk to 8 cm ($3\frac{1}{4}$ in)

Primary Features

Narrow pointed pale yellow-brown cap with a greasy surface, never expanding, and pale wavy stalk. Gills adnexed, brown with a white edge. Spore print purple brown.

Other Features

Like some other psilocybes this contains the hallucinogenic drug psilocybin and **can cause delirium**. **Mountain Moss Psilocybe** *(Ps. montana)* (**1**) is dark brown, with a hemispherical cap, opening out flat with a central umbo.

Habitat and Distribution

Liberty Cap: common in grassland, parks, by the roadside. Mountain Moss Psilocybe: common on heaths and moorland, but also grows on rich soil by the roadside.

Lookalikes

Avoid all 'little brown mushrooms'; **some are deadly**. **Psathyrella**: black spores; **Lawn Mower's Mushroom**; *Bolbitius*: shrivels rapidly, brown spores. **Mycena**: white spores; **Deadly Galerina**: brown spores.

Time of Appearance

August–November; April–October (**1**)

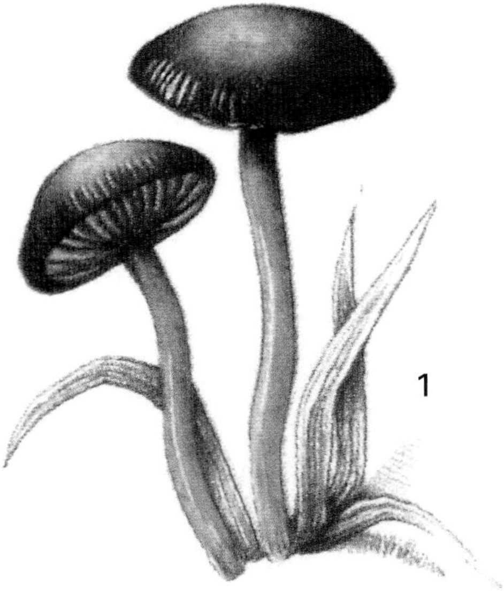

1

Here the Liberty Cap appears pale, but it often has a yellow-brown cap. As some small brown mushrooms are poisonous, it is wise not to eat any of them.

Sweating Mushroom

Cap 2–4 cm ($^{3}/_{4}$–$1^{1}/_{2}$ in); stalk to 4 cm ($1^{1}/_{2}$ in)

Clitocybe dealbata

Primary Features

Small creamy-white mushroom with pinky-brown markings on older caps. Gills thin, adnate decurrent, creamy, crowded. Stalk white and silky. Spore print white.

Other Features

A **highly poisonous** species which could be gathered in mistake for several edible mushrooms. It contains the toxin muscarine which produces sweating, blurred vision and involuntary muscle movements.

Habitat and Distribution

Common on lawns and in grass generally.

Lookalikes

There are several white clitocybes, characterized by thin decurrent gills and white spores, e.g. *Clit. Rivulosa*: wrinkled cap, **toxic**. **The Miller**: pink spores; **Buff Meadow Cap**: thick gills, white spores.

Time of Appearance

August–November

Fairy-Ring Champignon

Marasmius oreades

Cap 2–5 cm ($\frac{3}{4}$–2 in); stalk to 7 cm (2$\frac{3}{4}$ in)

Primary Features

A common mushroom forming large rings in lawns and pastures. Moist, bell-shaped rusty-brown cap flattens out and pales to yellowish brown. Stalk tough, felty. Spore print white.

Other Features

Like all *Marasmius* species, this tough mushroom quickly revives on moistening after drying out. Good to eat if the tough stalks are discarded but **take care not to confuse** with poisonous whitish clitocybes also common in grass.

Habitat and Distribution

Very common in lawns, pastures and by paths.

Lookalikes

Sweating Mushroom and *Clit. Rivulosa*; **Mycena** species also have white spores.

Time of Appearance

May–November

Fairy-ring Champignons are good to eat, even after becoming dried out. However, they must not be confused with other clitocybes, which are poisonous.

Deceiver

Laccaria laccata

Cap 1–6 cm ($\frac{1}{2}$–2$\frac{1}{2}$ in); stalk to 8 cm (3$\frac{1}{4}$ in)

Primary Features

Reddish-brown to pinkish-brown smooth cap soon becoming sunken in centre. Gills pale with a pinkish tinge, thick, slightly waxy and spaced quite far apart. Spore print white.

Other Features

A variable mushroom, common but often hard to identify. Gills adnate. **Inedible**. **Lawn Mower's Mushroom** *(Panaeolina foenisecii)* (**1**) has a brown bell-shaped cap, 1–2 cm ($\frac{1}{2}$–$\frac{3}{4}$ in), drying paler in centre. Brown gills adnate, mottled. Spores brown.

Habitat and Distribution

Deceiver: very common and widespread on heaths and in broad-leaved woods, also in sphagnum bogs. Lawn Mower's Mushroom: very common in lawns and short grass.

Lookalikes

Amethyst Deceiver: violet throughout when young and moist, drying paler, thick gills spaced far apart and white spores, in woods; **Mycena** spp; **Psathyrella** spp; *Hygrophorus* and **Hygrocybe** spp have waxy gills and white spores.

Time of Appearance

July–December

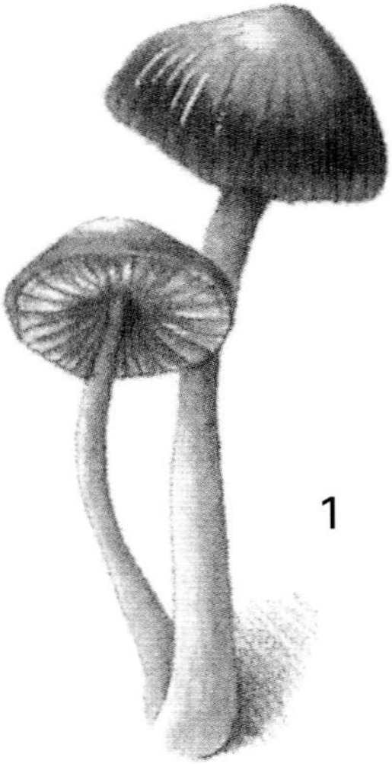

1

The Deceiver, as its name suggests, is hard to identify, despite being a common mushroom. The cap varies from reddish brown to pinkish brown in colour.

Buff Meadow Cap

Cuphophyllus (Camarophyllus) pratensis

Cap 5–10 cm (2–4 in); stalk to 5 cm (2 in)

Primary Features

A rather stout squat mushroom, with fleshy buff to dull-orange cap. The pale buff gills are waxy, widely spaced and run down and merge with stalk. Spore print white.

Other Features

An excellent edible mushroom. The surface of the cap is dry and matt and often cracks around the centre. The thick gills are thin-edged and have short gills interspersed between them. The stalk is stout, and a similar colour to gills.

Habitat and Distribution

Common and quite widespread in meadows, lawns, grassy copses and also in woods.

Lookalikes

Chanterelle: ridges on underside of cap, not gills, orange-yellow; **False Chanterelle**; *Cuph. niveus* and others: white, smaller, edible but **best avoided** for fear of confusion with toxic white clitocybes (e.g. **Sweating Mushroom**).

Time of Appearance

August–December

Look out for the Buff Meadow Cap, which is excellent to eat. It is a stout, squat mushroom and its cap ranges in colour from buff to dull orange.

St George's Mushroom

Cap 5–13 cm (2–$5\frac{1}{4}$ in); stalk to 8 cm ($3\frac{1}{4}$ in)

Calocybe gambosa

Primary Features

White to greyish-buff fleshy convex cap with an inrolled edge. Gills white to cream, narrow and crowded, sinuate. A 'mushroom' smell. Spore print white.

Other Features

This mushroom is found only in the spring, never in the autumn. Flesh firm and white. An excellent edible mushroom.

Habitat and Distribution

Quite common and widespread in grassy woodland glades, wood edges, under hedges. Sometimes forms large fairy-rings in grassland.

Lookalikes

Take care not to confuse with toxic white **clitocybes, Lead Poisoner** or **Deadly Inocybe**, which grow in similar situations, but which usually appear later.

Time of Appearance

April–June

Take care not to confuse the St George's Mushroom, which is great to eat, with the toxic white clitocybes species, the Lead Poisoner or the Deadly Inocybe.

Fried-Chicken Mushroom

Cap 4–12 cm ($1\frac{1}{2}$–$4\frac{3}{4}$ in); stalk to 12 cm ($4\frac{3}{4}$ in)

Lyophyllum decastes

Primary Features

Growing in clusters on ground often around stumps or buried roots. Smooth shiny yellowish-grey to reddish-brown cap, crowded white adnate gills. Stalk whitish. Spore print white.

Other Features

Although sometimes considered edible, this is **best avoided**. The caps begin convex and then flatten out and the gills become straw coloured with age. The thin white flesh is tough with a faint mealy smell.

Habitat and Distribution

Common and widespread in grassy copses, gardens, parks.

Lookalikes

L. fumosum: greyish gills, stems joined together at base, on rich soil, compost heaps;

L. connatum: glossy-white caps, white arched decurrent gills, white stalk, in clusters in grass; **Lead Poisoner**.

Time of Appearance

July–October

The Fried-chicken Mushroom is common in gardens and parks. It has a faint mealy smell, which may help to distinguish it from other species.

Weeping Widow

Psathyrella lacrymabunda

Cap 5–10 cm (2–4 in); stalk to 12 cm ($4^{3}/_{4}$ in)

Primary Features

Brown to blackish gills 'weep' black droplets. Grey-brown velvety or scaly cap with a woolly edge often blackened by spores. Ring-like marking from veil on stalk. Spores black.

Other Features

Gills adnate, mottled, with white edges. Fibrous stalk. Edible. One of the larger psathyrellas, some others are very small and delicate. The edge of young cap is attached to stalk by a fine veil in some, but not all, psathyrellas.

Habitat and Distribution

Very common and widespread in fields, on bare soil, beside paths, often in association with buried dead wood or roots.

Lookalikes

Ps. candolleana: creamy-white cap, splitting at edges, gills pale brownish lilac, stalk white, no ring, common on and around stumps, in nettle beds, copses; **Clustered Psathyrella**; **Cortinarius** species: brown spores; **Deceiver**.

Time of Appearance

April–November

The brown to blackish gills of the Weeping Widow 'weep' black droplets. The cap has a woolly edge and a ring-like marking on the stalk, from the veil.

Spring Agrocybe

Agrocybe praecox

Cap 4–6 cm ($1\frac{1}{2}$–$2\frac{1}{2}$ in); stalk to 10 cm (4 in)

Primary Features

Beige-brown cap fading in dull yellow grey. Shaggy margin to cap. Gills adnexed, crowded, whitish to dingy brown. Ring high on a slender fibrous stalk. Spore print dark brown.

Other Features

Although harmless and sometimes considered edible it is not of high quality and **should be avoided** for fear of confusion with other rather nondescript poisonous mushrooms. Flesh pale, with a smell of new-ground meal.

Habitat and Distribution

Common and widespread in grassy copses and thickets, lawns.

Lookalikes

A. dura: cap cracking; **Field Mushroom** and other *Agaricus* spp: free gills; **Poison Pie**: slimy caps.

Time of Appearance

April–July

Shaggy Ink-Cap or Lawyer's Wig

Coprinus comatus

Cap to 15 cm (6 in) high; stalk to 10 cm (4 in)

Primary Features

Shaggy white young cap eventually dissolves into an inky fluid as gills auto-digest from the edge of cap inwards. Crowded whitish gills turn black from tips. Black spores.

Other Features

Edible when all white. **Common Ink-cap** *(C. atramentarius)* **(1)** has a smoother grey cap, brownish in centre. Edible, but not with, or for a day or two after or before taking alcohol, when it **causes nasty symptoms** similar to the drug Antabuse.

Habitat and Distribution

Both are common and widespread, in clusters on pastures, lawns, by the roadside, by paths and on bare soil.

Lookalikes

Many, but not all, *Coprinus* species have gills that turn black and dissolve; **Mica Ink-cap**; **Field Mushroom** and other *Agaricus* spp, gills do not dissolve; **Parasol Mushroom** and **Shaggy Parasol**: gills do not dissolve.

Time of Appearance

April–November

1

The Shaggy Ink-cap or Lawyer's Wig dissolves into an inky fluid as it ages, because the gills begin to 'digest' themselves, starting from the outside.

Smooth Volvariella

Volvariella speciosa

Cap 8–15 cm (3¼–6 in); stalk to 18 cm (7¼ in)

Primary Features

A tall elegant mushroom whose silky white stalk has a sac-like volva at base but no ring. Cap whitish to grey brown. Gills pale, becoming salmon pink. Spore print pink.

Other Features

Although edible it is **not recommended**. The young mushrooms are completely enclosed in a white veil forming 'eggs' like those of amanitas. The sticky cap is at first conical and then opens out.

Habitat and Distribution

Quite common and widespread in grass in broad-leaved woods, on manured soil, garden compost heaps, pastures on rich soil.

Lookalikes

V. bombycina: shaggy or felty cap, grows on stumps or logs, especially of elm; **Amanitas**: ring as well as volva, white gills and spores; **Field Mushroom** and other *Agaricus* species: ring on stalk, no volva, purple-brown spore print.

Time of Appearance

June–October

Edible Mushrooms

These delicious wild cousins of the commercial mushroom are common in pastures and other grassland in early autumn. The genus *Agaricus* has white or brownish caps, a ring on stalk (but no volva), pinkish or greyish gills often becoming black, and a dark-brown spore print.

Field Mushroom *(Agaricus campestris)* (**1**): cap 3–10 cm (1¼–4 in), silky white when young. Ring narrow. Deep-pink gills become brownish. This tasty mushroom can be gathered in quantity from pastures in early autumn. *A. bitorquis*, two rings, edible. *A. macrosporus*: massive, cap to 30 cm (12 in), flesh flushes pinkish at base.

A. bisporus (**2**): is the wild form of the cultivated mushroom. It has a wider ring and pale-fawn cap.

Horse Mushroom *(Agaricus arvensis)* (**3**): cap 8–20 cm (3¼–8 in), creamy then russet. All parts stain yellow. Gills pinkish grey to dull brown. Fleshy ring on stalk. **Do not mistake** this good edible mushroom for the **Yellow-staining Mushroom**.

1
3
2

Yellow-Staining Mushroom

Cap 6–15 cm (2½–6 in); stalk to 15 cm (6 in)

Agaricus xanthodermus

Primary Features

Flesh at base of stalk stains deep golden yellow when this mushroom is cut lengthways. The silky white cap also turns yellow at edges and where damaged.

Other Features

This is **highly indigestible** and causes severe gastric upsets if eaten. The bright-yellow flesh at the base of the stalk is the main distinguishing feature. Like all *Agaricus* species the spore print is dark purplish brown.

Habitat and Distribution

Quite common and widespread in parks, gardens, roadsides and under broad-leaved trees in grassy places.

Lookalikes

Several good edible mushrooms also stain yellow or become yellow with age, such as *A. silvicola* in woods, and the **Horse Mushroom** in fields, but no other has the golden-yellow flesh at base of stalk.

Time of Appearance

July–October

Parasol Mushroom

Macrolepiota (Lepiota) procera Cap 12–25 cm (4¾–10 in); stalk to 25 cm (10 in)

Primary Features

This excellent edible mushroom has a thick double-edged ring which can be slid up and down the tall slender stalk, and a scaly parasol-shaped cap with shaggy edges. Gills cream.

Other Features

The brown cap surface breaks up into a central brown patch surrounded by brownish-beige scales on a paler ground. The scaly stalk has brown zones and a slightly swollen base. The pale flesh does not redden on cutting. Spore print white.

Habitat and Distribution

Common and widespread in pastures (sometimes forming fairy-rings), roadside verges, under hedges, and in grassy open woodland.

Lookalikes

Shaggy Parasol and lookalikes; **Lepiota**: ring fixed, generally smaller, **avoid, some are deadly**; *Leucoagaricus bresadolae*: in clusters on sawdust or compost, **toxic**; **Field Mushroom** and other *Agaricus* spp: brown spore print.

Time of Appearance

July–October

The Parasol Mushroom is excellent to eat. It has creamy gills, and a double-edged ring, that can usually be slid up and down the stalk.

Shaggy Parasol

Macrolepiota (Lepiota) rhacodes

Cap 12–18 cm ($4\frac{3}{4}$–$7\frac{1}{4}$ in); stalk to 12 cm ($4\frac{3}{4}$ in)

Primary Features

Pale-beige cap with coarse shaggy scales, greyish, beige, light or dark brown, and a smooth central area. Thick double ring moves on smooth stalk. Gills and spore print white.

Other Features

The white flesh turns saffron yellow when cut or bruised and the gills also discolour on bruising. The creamy-white stalk has a swollen base and bruises brownish. A good edible fungus.

Habitat and Distribution

Fairly common and widespread, in disturbed soil, on compost heaps, in grass and under conifers.

Lookalikes

The similar *M. venenata* has dark-brown scales, and a ring in a single piece, **toxic**; **Parasol Mushroom**; **Shaggy Ink-cap**; **Field Mushroom** and other *Agaricus* spp: dark-brown spore print.

Time of Appearance

July–November

The Shaggy Parasol, like the Parasol Mushroom, has a double ring that moves on the stalk. The cap and gills discolour on bruising, as does the stalk.

Deadly Lepiota

Lepiota helveola

Cap 5–8 cm (2–3¼ in); stalk to 5 cm (2 in)

Primary Features

Pinkish-brown flattish conical cap with rings of concentric scales on a paler ground. Gills pinkish. Fragile ring on a slender stalk. Spore print white.

Other Features

This typical small *Lepiota* is one of several similar species which are **deadly poisonous**. The stalks are smooth, generally ringed with irregular zones of brown. **Do not confuse** them with the larger **Parasol Mushroom**.

Habitat and Distribution

This and similar species are rare. Deadly Lepiota grows in urban copses in warm places, occasionally found in southeastern England. Others are found in various habitats.

Lookalikes

L. brunneoincarnata: more purplish in colour, no distinct ring, grassy copses, **deadly**; *L. lilacea*: pale purplish-brown cap, in gardens, **toxic**; *L. pseudohelveola*: finer scales on cap, under broad-leaved trees, **toxic**.

Time of Appearance

July–October

Pearl-Studded Puffball

Fruitbody 4–6 cm (1½–2½ in) diameter

Lycoperdon perlatum

Primary Features

Club-shaped thin-walled white fruitbody is firm at first, then soft, puffing out a cloud of powdery spores if pressed. Outer surface covered with small blunt spines.

Other Features

In this common puffball the spore mass becomes olive green at maturity, and the fruitbody discolours to a dirty yellowish brown and loses its spines. Edible when still white and firm throughout.

Habitat and Distribution

Very common and widespread on the ground in pastures, parks and woods.

Lookalikes

Pear-shaped Puffball: on wood; *Calvatia excipuliformis*: larger, spore-filled head on stout stalk; *L. echinatum*: spines 3–4 mm (⅛ in); **Common Puffball**; *Bovisa plumbea*: surface flakes off exposing grey inner wall; **Earthballs**: hard.

Time of Appearance

July–November

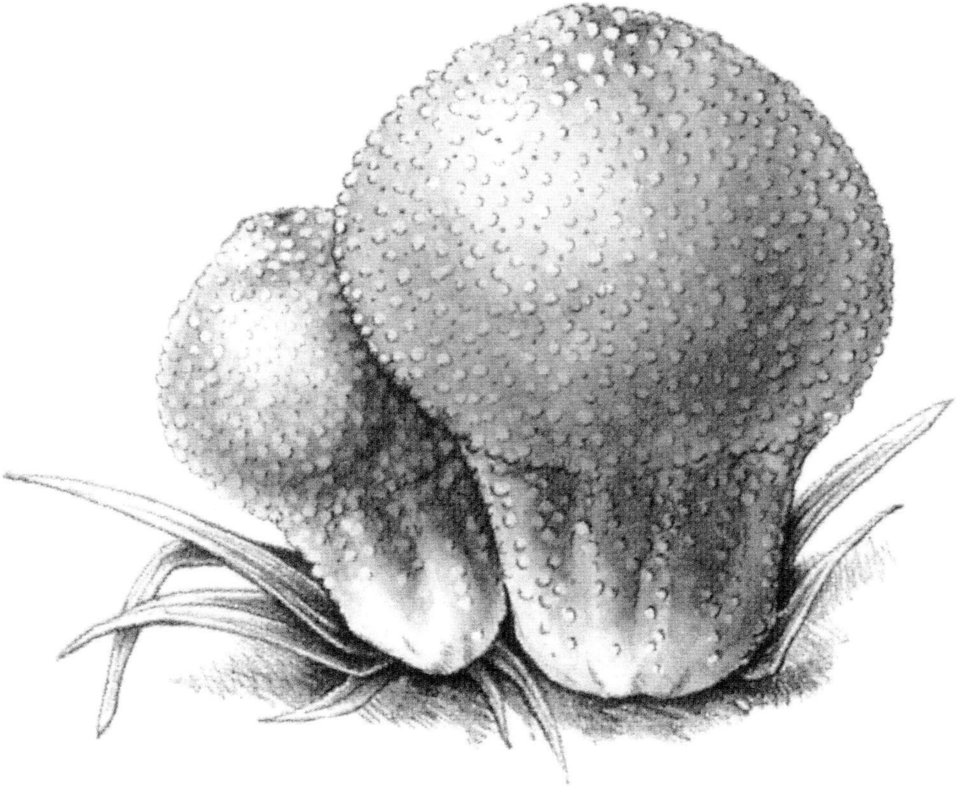

When still white and firm the Pearl-studded Puffball is edible. As it ages the fruitbody becomes a dirty yellowish brown and the spores become olive green.

Giant Puffball

Lagermannia gigantea

Fruitbody to 40 cm (16 in) diameter

Primary Features

This enormous puffball can weigh several kilos. It has a slightly flaky white outer surface. The internal spore mass is white becoming brown and powdery.

Other Features

Good to eat when still white and firm throughout. **Common Puffball** *(Vascellum pratense)* (**1**) is smaller (3–6 cm or $1\frac{1}{4}$–$2\frac{1}{2}$ in) and the spore mass is delimited from the sterile spongy base by a distinct membrane. Edible when young.

Habitat and Distribution

The Giant Puffball is locally common, in fertile pastures, gardens, hedgerows. The Common Puffball is very common and widespread in lawns, pastureland and grassy sand dunes.

Lookalikes

Other **Puffballs**; *Bovista plumbea*: white outer surface flakes off leaving bluish-grey inner wall; **Earthballs**: hard and leathery throughout.

Time of Appearance

August–September; July–November (**1**)

1

The fruitbody of the Giant Puffball can grow up to a vast 40 cm (16 in) in diameter and can be found in pastures, gardens and hedgerows.

Cup Fungi

Peziza vesiculosa

Fruitbody 6–8 cm ($2\frac{1}{2}$–$3\frac{1}{4}$ in) diameter

Primary Features

The pale-brown fruitbody is at first round, becoming cup-shaped with an incurved edge. The inner surface (which bears the spores) is yellowish, the outer surface fawn.

Other Features

It is **best not to eat** this or similar fungi. Although some are edible after cooking, others are **highly poisonous**. The cups of *Aleuria aurantia* (**1**), the **Orange-peel Fungus**, are 6–12 cm ($2\frac{1}{2}$–$4\frac{1}{4}$ in) across, and downy on the pale outer surface. Edible.

Habitat and Distribution

P. vesiculosa is rather uncommon, growing on manure heaps and rich soil. The Orange-peel Fungus is more common, growing on paths, bare gravel and bare soil.

Lookalikes

There are many cup fungi, often brightly coloured. *P. succosa*: bright-yellow juice from cut flesh, in woods; *P. badia*: dark-olive inner surface; *Scutellinia scutellata*: orange inner surface fringed with black hairs.

Time of Appearance

August–April; September–January (**1**)

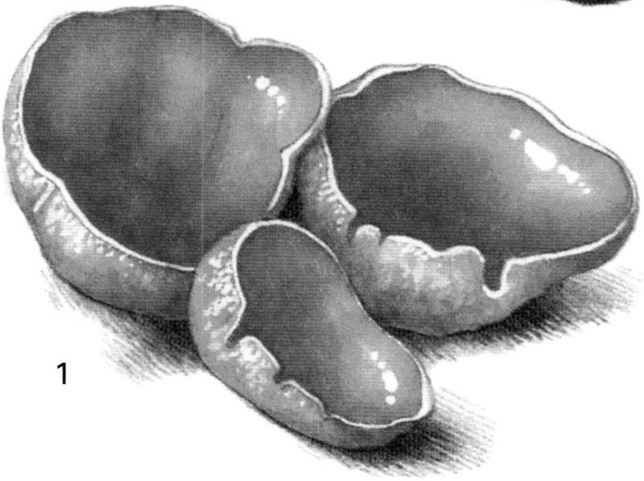

1

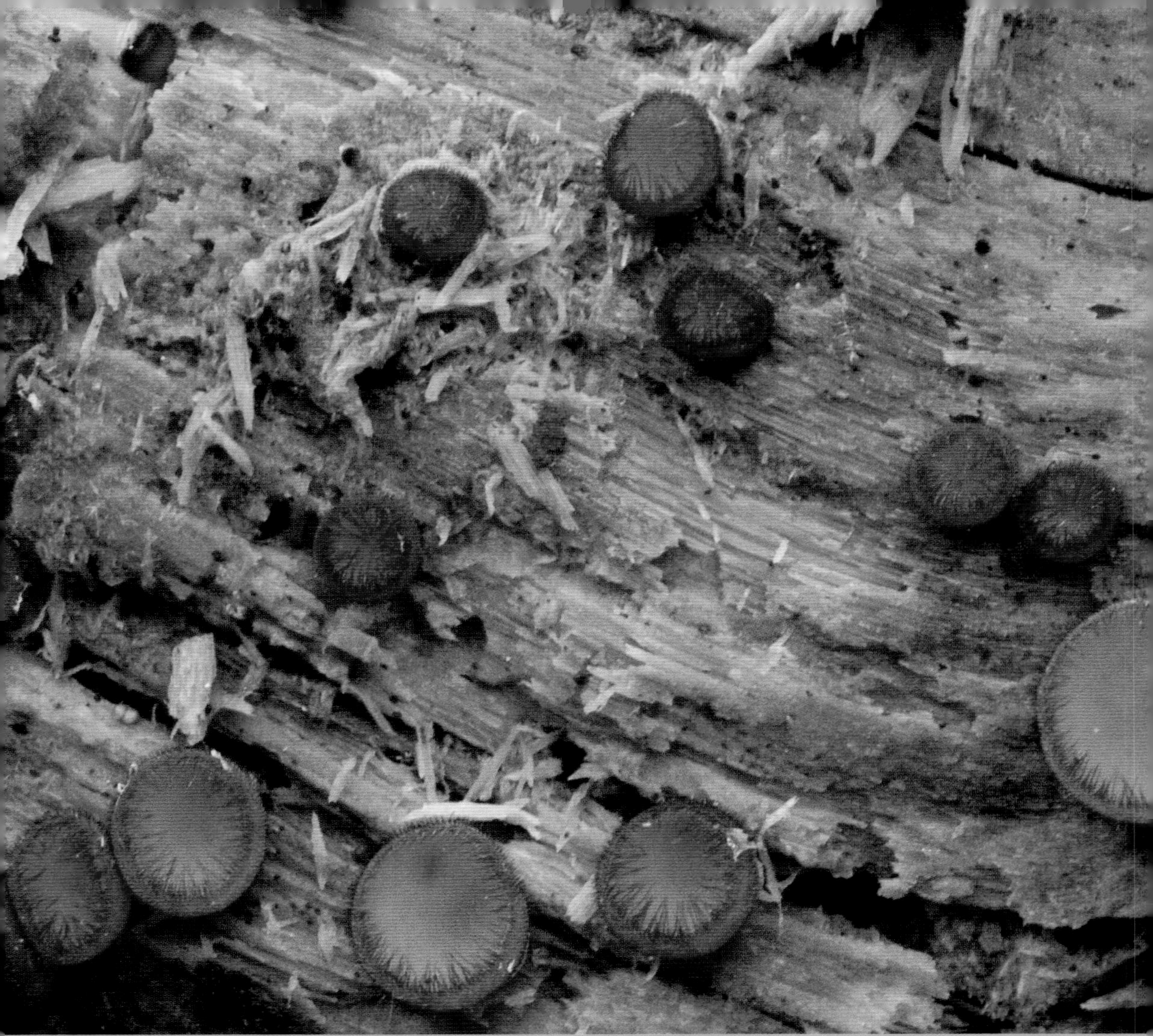

It is advisable not to eat Cup Fungi because although some of the similar species are edible once cooked, others remain highly poisonous.

Bear's Head Tooth

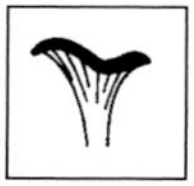

Hericium clathroides (coralloides)

Fruitbody to 40 cm (16 in) across

Primary Features

The brittle, coral-like fruitbody bears numerous long hanging spines 6–10 mm ($\frac{1}{4}$–$\frac{1}{2}$ in) long, whose surfaces carry the spores. Creamy to ivory white at first; tough and pinkish with age.

Other Features

This striking fungus is edible when young. The flesh is brittle and white but becomes tough in older specimens, although the spines themselves often remain edible and good.

Habitat and Distribution

Rather uncommon, on dead trunks of fir and of beech and other broad-leaved trees.

Lookalikes

The similar *Creolophus cirrhatus* consists of a series of flat white caps arising from a common base and bearing yellowish hanging spines on the lower surfaces. Not worth eating.

Time of Appearance

October–November

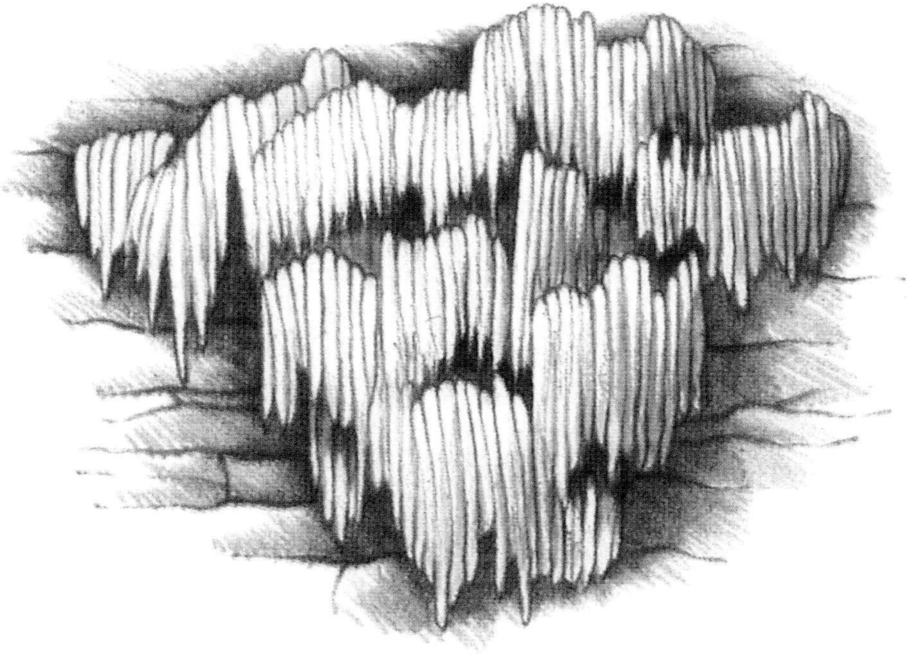

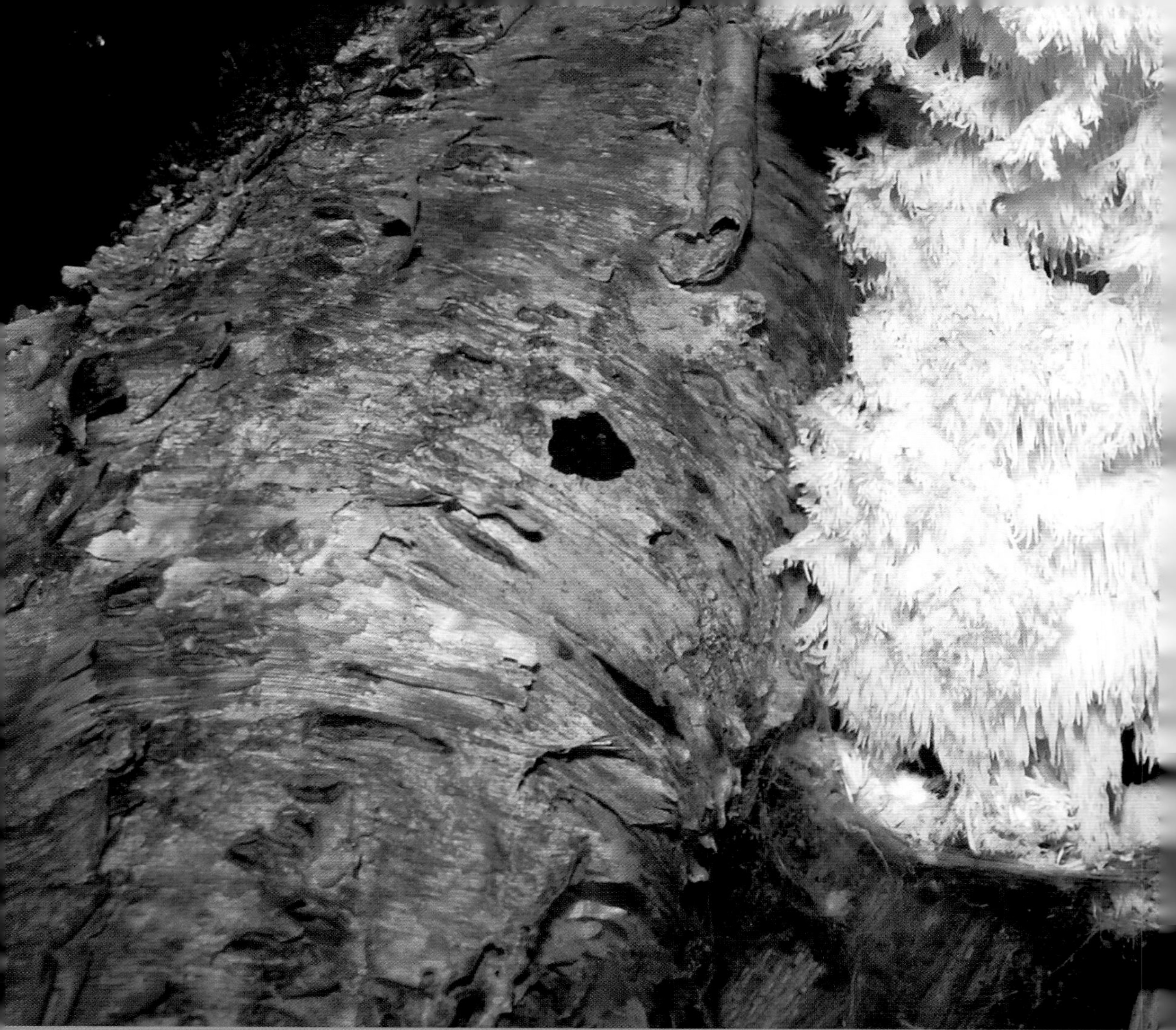

The Bear's Head Tooth can amass a fruitbody of up to 40 cm (16 in) in diameter, despite each of the numerous species being very small.

Ganoderma

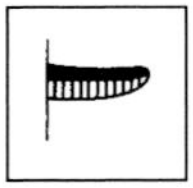

Ganoderma applanatum

Cap 15–50 cm (6–20 in) across

Primary Features

Growing as a series of 'brackets', the hard grey-brown bumpy upper surface becomes covered in a layer of rusty spores from the cap above. White undersurface turns brown when scratched.

Other Features

The upper surface is shiny before it becomes dusty with spores. The **Birch Polypore** *(Piptoporus betulinus)* (**1**) (10–15 cm or 4–6 in across) has a smooth matt greyish-brown upper surface, white pores and flesh underneath. Spores white.

Habitat and Distribution

Ganoderma: on dead trunks of broad-leaved trees and also on living trees, causing heart rot. Birch Polypore: on birch, causing heart rot, also on dead birches, common.

Lookalikes

G. lucidum: shiny reddish top, stalked, rare; **Red-belted Polypore**; *Daedalea quercina*: corky grey-brown top, brown below, broad pores; *Heterobasidion annosum*: thin cap, top dark brown, white below, often at base of conifers.

Time of Appearance

All year round

1

The Ganoderma is often found on the dead trunks of broad-leaved trees, but it can also be found on living trees. The mushrooms grow in bracket shapes.

Poor Man's Beefsteak

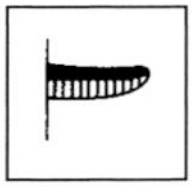

Cap 15–40 cm (6–16 in)

Fistulina hepatica

Primary Features

The cut flesh of this leathery-topped shelf fungus yields a red juice and looks and feels like red meat.

Other Features

Rough reddish-brown top, yellowish tubes on underside. Although edible after boiling, it does not live up to its name. **Red-belted Polypore** *(Fomitopsis pinicola)* (**1**) is a hard-topped bracket, reddish brown above, white below.

Habitat and Distribution

Poor Man's Beefsteak: quite common on living oaks, causing 'brown oak' staining in the wood; Red-belted Polypore; rarer, mainly on conifers, causing heart rot.

Lookalikes

Phellinus igniarius: furrowed and cracked hard upper surface is grey to black with a velvety margin, underside yellow to brown-grey, on broad-leaved trees.

Time of Appearance

August–November; all year (**1**)

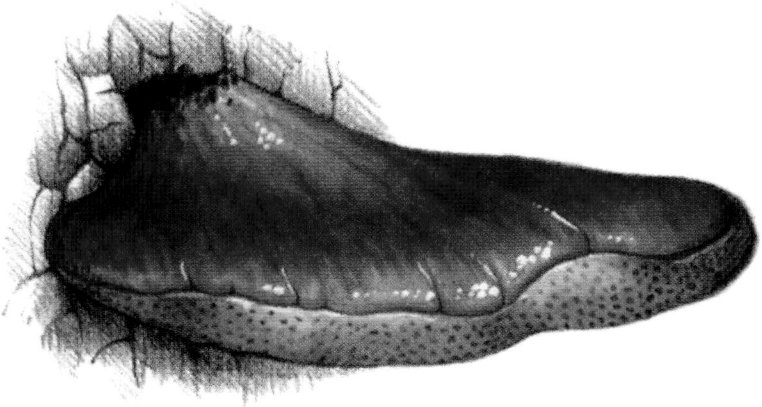

1

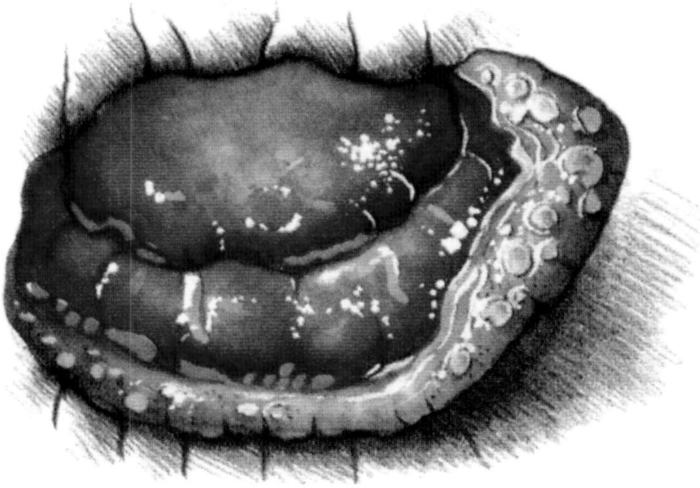

Unfortunately the Poor Man's Beefsteak, although edible if boiled, does not have such a good flavour. It is commonly found living on oak trees.

Dryad's Saddle

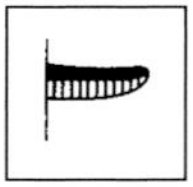

Polyporus squamosus

Cap 15–30 cm (6–12 in) across

Primary Features

Circular to kidney-shaped polypore with a lateral stalk and a soft leathery surface breaking up into rings of pale to dark-brown scales on a yellowish ground. White pores.

Other Features

This is edible when very young and tender, but soon becomes tough. The white flesh has a faint smell of honey.

Habitat and Distribution

Very common on trunks, stumps and logs of broad-leaved trees.

Lookalikes

Polyporus species and relatives have soft leathery tops in contrast to the woody bracket fungi. *P. varius*: smooth brownish-yellow cap; the multiple-capped *Grifola frondosa* is reported to smell of 'mice, hops and cold mashed potato'.

Time of Appearance

April–December

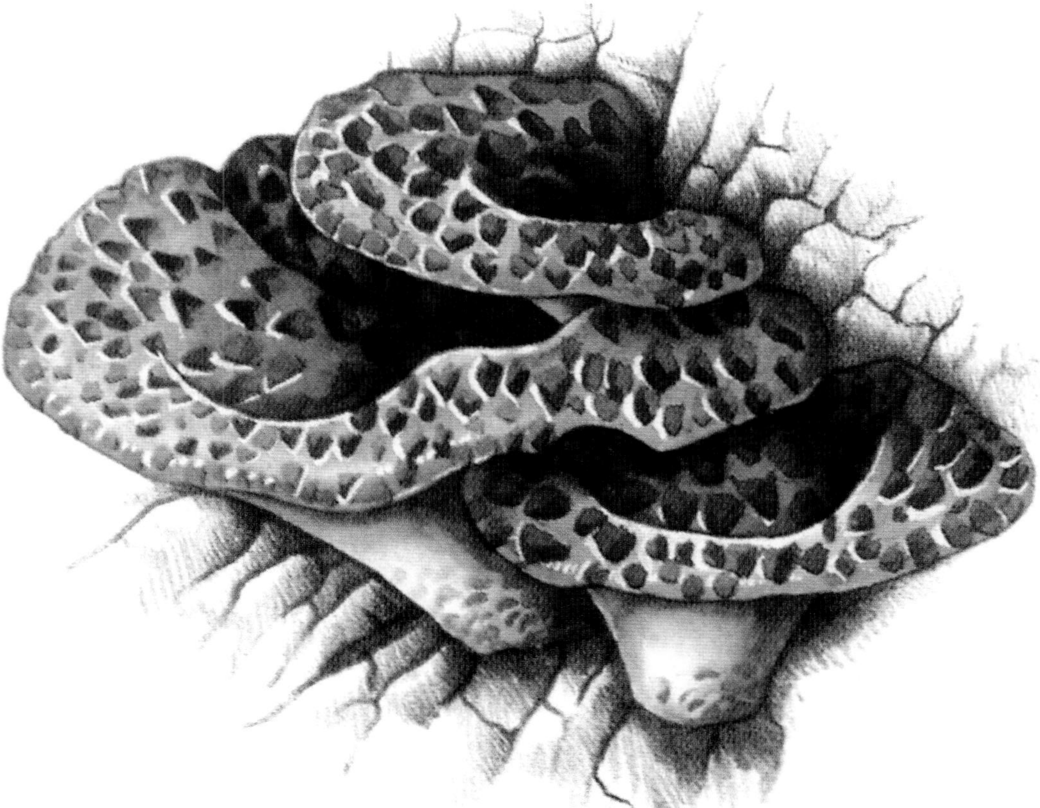

The Dryad's Saddle is edible when young, but becomes too tough as it ages. It has a faint honey scent and is commonly found on trunks of broad-leaved trees.

Turkey Tail

Trametes versicolor

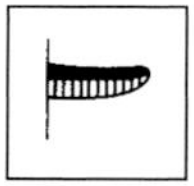

Cap 3–5 cm (1¼–2 in) across

Primary Features

Thin silky-topped lobed-edged brackets are concentrically zoned in shades of olive, purple, green, grey and black. Underside whitish.

Other Features

Logs are sometimes covered almost completely in the brackets of this common species. It is one of numerous small thin bracket fungi that attack dead wood or sometimes cause disease in living trees.

Habitat and Distribution

Ubiquitous on dead wood of all sorts.

Lookalikes

T. gibbosa: top white and felty, often with green growth of algae in centre; *Trichaptum abietinum*: thin elastic caps, velvety greyish top with violet tinge at edges, on softwood; *Daedalopsis confragosa*: pale-brown zoned caps, white below.

Time of Appearance

All year round, but annual only

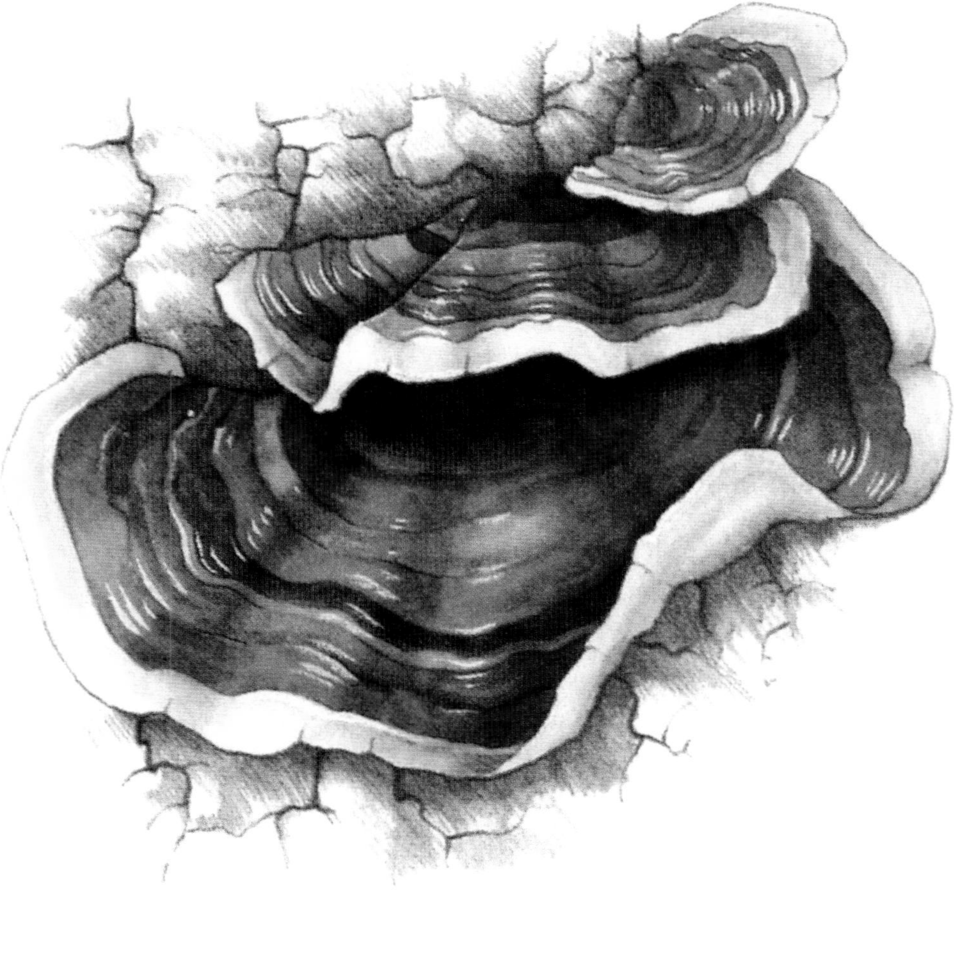

The concentric colour zones of the Turkey Tail can be olive, purple, green, grey and black. They live on dead wood and can grow to completely cover logs.

Oyster Fungus

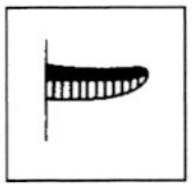

Pleurotus ostreatus

Cap 8–15 cm ($3\frac{1}{4}$–6 in) across

Primary Features

Fleshy semicircular or shell-shaped caps growing directly out of wood or attached with a very short (1 cm or $\frac{1}{2}$ in) stalk. Upper surface bluish grey fading to brown, white gills below.

Other Features

A good edible fungus when young, with firm white flesh and a mushroom smell. Cap has a waxy sheen when young and colour can vary from almost black to dark brown in older specimens. Gills decurrent. Spore print lilac.

Habitat and Distribution

Common on dead trunks and branches of all kinds. Can also attack living broad-leaved trees, and more rarely conifers.

Lookalikes

Other common (but **not edible**) bracket fungi with gills are *P. cornucopiae*: whitish to beige, becoming funnel-shaped; *P. pulmonarius*: thin white brackets with lobed edges; *P. dryinus*: white scaly cap, cylindrical stalk.

Time of Appearance

All year round

The Oyster Fungus is shell-shaped, with very short stalks. The upper surface of the caps are bluish grey with white gills below.

Velvet Foot

Flammulina velutipes

Cap 5–10 cm (2–4 in); stalk to 6 cm ($2\frac{1}{2}$ in)

Primary Features

Clusters of flat, sticky, honey-coloured to bright red-brown caps on dark-brown velvety stalks. Gills yellowish, adnexed. Spore print white.

Other Features

The caps are edible after the slimy skin is removed but are not of high quality. **Sulphur Tuft** *(Hypholoma fasciculare)* **(1)** has a yellow cap (4–8 cm or $1\frac{1}{2}$–$3\frac{1}{4}$ in), sulphur-yellow gills turning black, yellow stalk and brown spore print. **Inedible**.

Habitat and Distribution

Both are very common and widespread, growing on stumps and dead wood of broad-leaved trees (Sulphur Tuft also on conifers).

Lookalikes

Honey Fungus; *Philiota alnicola*: narrow ring on stalk, brown spores, on alder and birch wood; other relatively common yellow pholiotas on wood have scaly caps, e.g. *P. squarrosa*.

Time of Appearance

September–March

1

Velvet Foot is very common and is found on the stumps of broad-leaved trees. The caps are edible if the slimy skin is removed, but are not very tasty.

Common Mycena

Mycena galericulata

Cap 2–5 cm ($\frac{3}{4}$–2 in); stalk to 8 cm ($3\frac{1}{4}$ in)

Primary Features

Conical pale grey-brown cap flattens out on ageing. Gills white becoming pinkish. Stalk tough, smooth, same colour as cap, 'rootlike' at base. Spore print white.

Other Features

Inedible. Clustered Psathyrella *(Psathyrella hydrophila)* (**1**) has a moist chestnut-brown cap drying to pale yellow in centre. Unstriated shaggy edge. Faint ring on white stalk. Gills adnate, greyish brown. Spore print black.

Habitat and Distribution

Both are common and widespread, growing in clusters on stumps of broad-leaved trees.

Lookalikes

Deadly Galerina and lookalikes; *M. polygramma*: pale-greyish caps, grey stalk with fine greyish lines, in tufts; *M. inclinata*: reddish-brown cap and stalk, rancid smell, in clusters; *Ps. candolleana* also grows on wood.

Time of Appearance

May–November; August–December (**1**)

1

The Common Mycena has a pale conical cap that flattens on ageing. The gills age from white to pinkish, while the stalk has a root-like appearance at the base.

Deadly Galerina

Galerina unicolor (marginata) Cap 4–8 cm ($1\frac{1}{2}$–$3\frac{1}{4}$ in); stalk to 6 cm ($2\frac{1}{2}$ in)

Primary Features

Sticky date-brown cap with darker striated edge soon expands and flattens out, drying a dull yellow brown. Small ring on stalk, which is darker below ring. Spore print brown.

Other Features

The narrow adnate gills are crowded, and are at first yellowish, becoming pale russet. The stem is fibrous. This is a **highly poisonous** mushroom and should not be eaten.

Habitat and Distribution

Common and widespread, growing in tufts on conifer stumps and other woody debris.

Lookalikes

Kuehneromyces mutabilis: very similar, but stem sheathed in a woolly layer up to a ring, on broad-leaved stumps, not toxic; **Clustered Psathyrella**; *pholiotas* ring more distinct, scaly stalk; **Honey Fungus**.

Time of Appearance

September–November

The name of the Deadly Galerina is very appropriate, as it is extremely poisonous. On ageing the cap flattens out and dries a dull yellow-brown colour.

Mica Ink-Cap

Coprinus micaceus

Cap 2–4 cm (3/4–1 1/2 in); stalk to 8 cm (3 1/4 in)

Primary Features

Fragile, bell-shaped, tawny-brown cap is grooved from edge almost to centre and the central surface is covered with minute glistening granules which soon disappear.

Other Features

Gills fragile, crowded, brown to black, eventually dissolving but not to the same extent as the Ink-caps. The edge of the cap is somewhat lobed and often splits as the mushroom ages. Stalk white with glistening granules near base. Spores black.

Habitat and Distribution

Very common everywhere on stumps and logs. When growing on ground it is in contact with buried wood or dead roots. Usually in clusters.

Lookalikes

C. domesticus: very similar, granules on the slightly paler cap are more prominent and last longer; *C. disseminatus*: cap 0.5–1 cm (1/4–1/2 in), pale brown or grey, velvety, fragile, grooved, gills not dissolving; **psathyrellas**.

Time of Appearance

All year round, especially May–December

Like all Ink-caps, the cap of the Mica Ink-cap dissolves itself, from its outer edges, as it ages. It is a fragile mushroom with a delicate grooved cap.

Purple and Yellow Agaric

Cap 8–15 cm ($3\frac{1}{4}$–6 in); stalk to 8 cm ($3\frac{1}{4}$ in)

Tricholomopsis rutilans

Primary Features

Golden-yellow cap speckled with minute purplish scales, especially in the centre. The adnexed, crowded gills are orange yellow. Stalk yellow. Spore print white.

Other Features

Although harmless this common mushroom is not worth eating. The yellow flesh smells faintly of damp wood and has a slightly bitter taste. The yellow cap becomes a rusty brown with age.

Habitat and Distribution

Common and widespread on and around conifer stumps and fence posts.

Lookalikes

Tr. decora: cap golden yellow, only slightly speckled with olive; **tricholomas**: on ground; **Honey Fungus**: ring on stalk, brown scales on cap; *A. tabescens*: like **Honey Fungus** but no ring, in dense tufts on stumps, such as oak.

Time of Appearance

August–November

The Purple and Yellow Agaric looks very striking but tastes unremarkable. The flesh is bitter and smells slightly of damp wood.

Jack O'Lantern

Omphalotus olearius

Cap 8–15 cm (3¼–6 in); stalk to 8 cm (3¼ in)

Primary Features

A bright-orange fungus, becoming duller and darker with age. Cap soon flat or sunken with a central knob. Gills narrow, crowded, sharp edged, decurrent. Pale-cream spore print.

Other Features

This **poisonous** fungus superficially resembles a larger version of the Chanterelle. The smooth cap eventually turns brownish. Edges of cap incurved.

Habitat and Distribution

Growing in clusters on wood. Very rare in Britain, only in southeastern England. More common in southern Europe, Sweet Chestnut being one of its preferred hosts.

Lookalikes

Chanterelle: grows on ground; **False Chanterelle**; grows on ground or on woody debris.

Time of Appearance

July–November

The Jack O'Lantern is a similar shape to the Chanterelle, and is a similar colour. However, they should not be confused, as this species is poisonous.

Spindle Shank

Collybia fusipes

Cap 5–10 cm (2–4 in); stalk to 15 cm (6 in)

Primary Features

Tough, flattened, grooved, spindle-shaped stalk supports a shiny reddish-brown cap. Gills thick, greyish becoming speckled with brown, far apart. Spore print white.

Other Features

The swollen stalks, brown at base, paler above, arise from a common base within the wood on which they grow. The cap is often rather irregularly shaped and sometimes develops rusty spots. The young caps only are edible after cooking.

Habitat and Distribution

Common and widespread, growing in tufts on stumps or arising from roots, especially of beech and oak.

Lookalikes

Collybia confluens: on the ground, smaller, hairy pinkish stalks, **inedible**; **Russet Shank**. Collybias have tough stalks and white spores.

Time of Appearance

July–November

Honey Fungus

Armillaria mellea

Cap 4–25 cm ($1\frac{1}{2}$–10 in); stalk to 12 cm ($4\frac{3}{4}$ in)

Primary Features

Flattish honey-coloured cap with an incurved edge is covered with fine brown scales in centre. Gills white, crowded, adnate or decurrent. Large ring on stalk, Spores white.

Other Features

It spreads by thick black 'bootlaces' *(rhizomorphs)* running under the bark of trees it infects. **Edible with care**. **Orange Pholiota** *(Gymnopilus spectabilis)* (**1**) cap 8–15 cm ($3\frac{1}{4}$–6 in), velvety, rich orange brown, stalk thick, fibrous.

Habitat and Distribution

Honey Fungus: very common in tufts on stumps and above roots, a serious parasite of many trees; Orange Pholiota: less common, clustered at base of broad-leaved trees or on stumps.

Lookalikes

A. tabescens: similar to Honey Fungus, no ring, more southerly distribution;

other pholiotas: scaly stalks, often scaly caps, spore print brown.

Time of Appearance

June–December

1

The Honey Fungus is a parasitical fungus that spreads thick black 'bootlaces' under the bark of the trees that it infests.

Round-Stalked Agrocybe

Cap 4–12 cm ($1\frac{1}{2}$–$4\frac{3}{4}$ in); stalk to 12 cm ($4\frac{3}{4}$ in)

Agrocybe aegerita

Primary Features

Smooth silky beige cap with yellowish centre becomes wrinkled and cracked. Gills adnate decurrent, pale, becoming dull brown. Ring on stalk soon becomes shrivelled. Spores brown.

Other Features

Pale flesh has a pleasant smell. Edible. Stalk white, greyish at base, covered with small fibres. **Slimy Beech Cap** *(Oudemansiella mucida)* (**1**) has slimy translucent white cap and gills. Spores white. Edible after cooking.

Habitat and Distribution

Round-stalked Agrocybe: in clusters on stumps or dead wood of many broad-leaved trees; Slimy Beech Cap: only on dead trunks or branches of beech.

Lookalikes

Honey Fungus; *Kuehneromyces mutabilis*: two-toned brown cap, which changes colour on drying, no ring on stalk.

Time of Appearance

May–November; August–November (**1**)

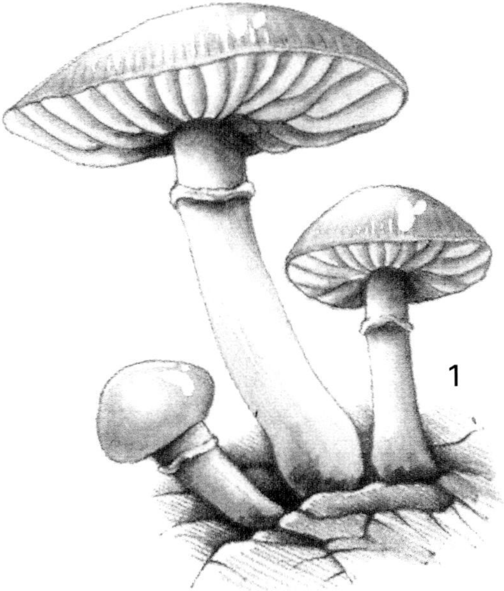

1

Fawn Mushroom

Pluteus cervinus (atricapillus) Cap 3–15 cm (1¼–6 in); stalk to 12 cm (4¾ in)

Primary Features

Greyish-brown cap with darker striations radiating from centre. Gills crowded, free, white becoming pinkish. Stalk white, with brown fibres. Spore print pink.

Other Features

The stalk is slightly thickened at the base. The cap is bell-shaped at first, then opening out with a central knob. Flesh pale and smelling faintly of radishes. Edible but poor.

Habitat and Distribution

Very common and widespread on fallen trunks and stumps, especially of broad-leaved trees, and on piles of sawdust.

Lookalikes

Other *Pluteus* spp also grow on wood. Cap surface scaly, fibrous, velvety or shaggy, stems fibrous, gills white to pinkish, free, spore print pink. Some entolomas are very similar, but grow on the ground and have attached gills.

Time of Appearance

All year around

The bell-shaped cap of the Fawn Mushroom opens out. The pale flesh smells of radishes and is edible but not noteworthy.

Pear-Shaped Puffball

Fruitbody to 4 cm (1½ in) diameter

Lycoperdon pyriforme

Primary Features

Beige or yellowish pear-shaped rough-surfaced fruitbodies grow in clusters. Apex slightly pointed with a central pore through which the spores are released.

Other Features

This is the only puffball that grows on wood. The interior spore mass is white, becoming yellowish and powdery as the spores mature.

Habitat and Distribution

Common and widespread on stumps, fallen trunks and buried wood, usually of broad-leaved trees.

Lookalikes

L. lividum is similar but rounder and grows in grass; **Pearl-studded Puffball**; **Earthballs** are hard and leathery throughout.

Time of Appearance

August–November

The Pear-shaped Puffball is identifiable as it is the only puffball that grows on wood. The fruitbodies are small, measuring up to 4 cm ($1\frac{1}{2}$ in) in diameter.

Judas's Ear

Auricularia auriculae-judae

Fruitbody 5–12 cm (2–4¾ in) across

Primary Features

Ear-shaped greyish-brown to reddish-brown fruitbody has a velvety outer surface and firm jelly-like flesh when young and/or moistened. The inner surface bears vein-like ridges.

Other Features

The whole fruitbody becomes more regularly shaped with age and is bone hard when completely dry. It is a good edible fungus. **Witches Butter** *(Tremella mesenterica)* (**1**) is golden orange and of a softer consistency when moist; shrivelled and hard when dry.

Habitat and Distribution

Judas's Ear: common on dead branches of elder, occurring more rarely on other broad-leaved trees. Witches Butter: common and widespread on dead branches.

Lookalikes

A. mesenterica: irregularly lobed caps, whitish shaggy upper surface, on logs and stumps of elm; *Exidia truncata*: small, blackish, rounded, firm gelatinous flesh, minute warts on upper surface, especially on dead wood of oak.

Time of Appearance

All year round especially October–December

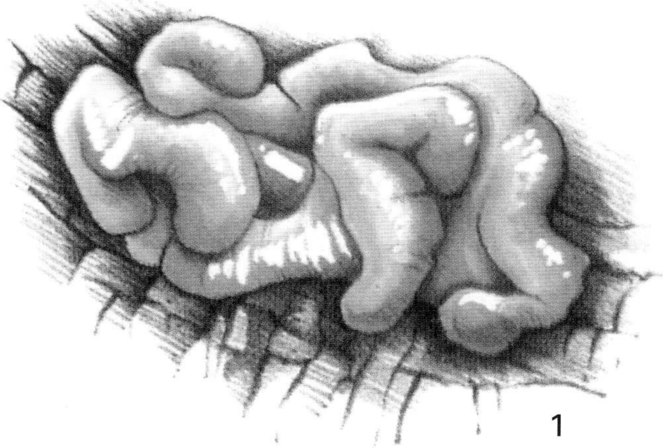

1

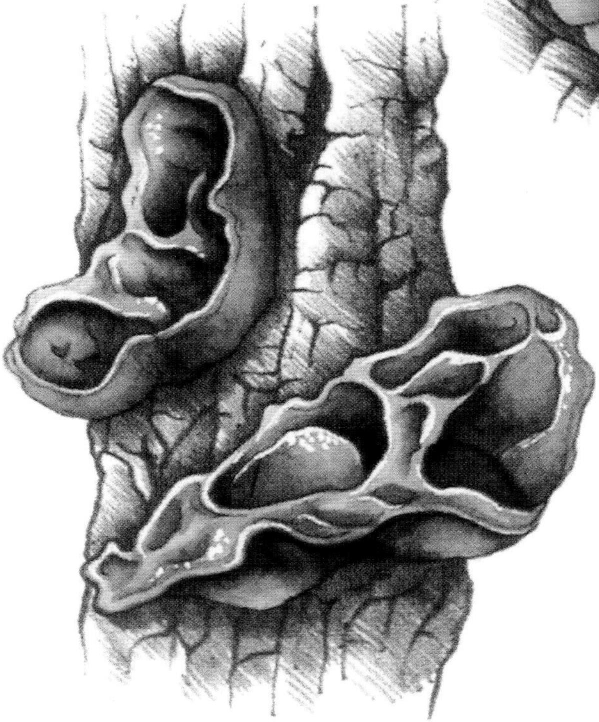

Carbon Balls

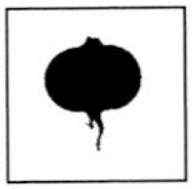

Daldinia concentrica

Fruitbody 2–6 cm ($\frac{3}{4}$–$2\frac{1}{2}$ in) diameter

Primary Features

Hard, rounded, persistent fruitbodies, with a dull surface, at first dark brown becoming black, resembling burnt buns. When cut open, they show concentric silvery rings.

Other Features

This fungus often appears on dead branches after fires. The **Bird's Nest Fungus** *(Cyathus striatus)* (**1**), 0.5–1 cm ($\frac{1}{4}$–$\frac{1}{2}$ in) across, has a cup-shaped fruitbody with a fluted inner surface containing 10–12 small grey 'eggs' which contain the spores.

Habitat and Distribution

Carbon Balls: common on dead branches of broad-leaved trees, especially Ash. Bird's Nest Fungus: quite common on fallen branches and rotten wood.

Lookalikes

Exidia glandulosa is smaller than Carbon Balls, with a firm jelly-like consistency. Of the other Bird's Nest Fungi, *C. olla* has a smooth inner face to 'nest', *Crucibulum laeve* has a more cylindrical 'nest' and creamy-yellow 'eggs'.

Time of Appearance

All year round; March–November (**1**)

1

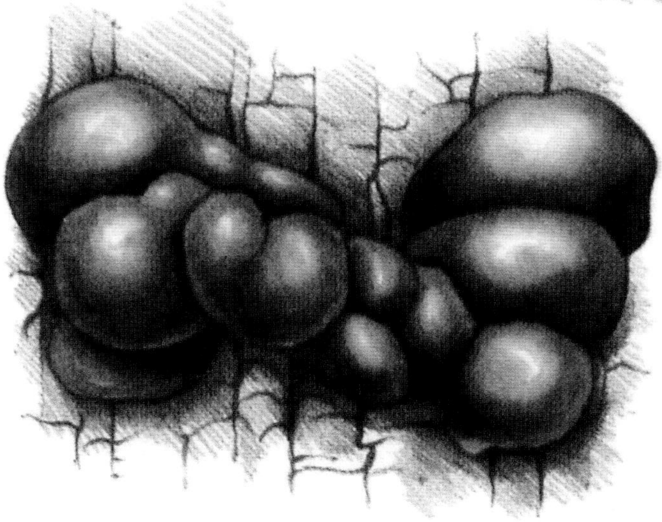

The hard fruitbodies of Carbon Balls become black and resemble burnt buns, with their dark, dull, rounded surfaces.

Further Reading

Carluccio, A., *Complete Mushroom Book: The Quiet Hunt*, Quadrille Publishing Ltd., 2005

Courtenay, B., *Field Guide to Mushrooms and Their Relatives*, Van Most, Reinhold, 1984

Dickson, G., *Mushrooms and Toadstools of Britain and Europe*, New Holland Publishers Ltd., 2002

Eppinger, M., *Field Guide to Mushrooms and Other Fungi of Britain and Europe*, New Holland Publishers Ltd., 2006

Harding, P. et al, *Edible Mushrooms (Collins How to ID)*, Collins, 1996

Jordan, M., *Encyclopedia of Fungi of Britain and Europe*, Frances Lincoln Publishers, 2004

Jordan, P., *The Practical Mushroom Encyclopedia: Identifying, Picking and Cooking with Mushrooms*, Southwater, 2000

Jordan, P. and Wheeler, S., *The Ultimate Mushroom Book: The Complete Guide to Identifying, Picking and Using Mushrooms*, Smithmark Publishing, 1995

Keizer, G.J., *The Complete Encyclopedia of Mushrooms*, Rebo Productions, 1998

Laessoe, T., *Mushrooms (Smithsonian Handbooks)*, DK Publishing, 2002

Lamaison, J.L. and Polese, J.M., *The Great Encyclopedia of Mushrooms*, Konemann, 2006

Pegler, D., *The Easy Edible Mushroom Guide*, Aurum Press Ltd., 1999

Pegler, D., *Kingfisher Field Guide to the Mushrooms and Toadstools of Britain and Europe*, Kingfisher Books Ltd., 1990

Phillips, R., *Mushrooms*, Macmillan, 2006

Kibby, G., *Philip's Guide to Mushrooms and Toadstools of Britain and Europe*, Philips, 2006

Schwab, A., *Mushrooming Without Fear*, Merlin Unwin Books, 2006

Spooner, B., *Mushrooms and Toadstools (Collins Wild Guide)*, HarperCollins, 2005

Underhill, J.E., *Guide to Western Mushrooms*, Hancock House Publishers Ltd., 1996

Picture Credits

Courtesy of Amanita Photolibrary: 20–21, 26–27, 48–49, 90–91, 118–19, 126–27, 130–31, 144–45, 148–49, 158–59, 162–63, 180–81, 188–89, 196–97, 226–27, 230–31, 234–35, 254–55, 262–63, 280–81, 320–21, 328–29, 332–33, 348–49, 352–53, 368–69, 372–73, 378–79.

Courtesy of NHPA/Photoshot: Matt Bain: 44–45; Simon Booth: 86–87, 176–77; Gerry Cambridge: 114–15; Laurie Campbell: 104–05, 170–71, 216–17; Nigel Dennis: 340–41; Martin Garwood: 30–31, 94–95, 122–23, 152–53, 166–67, 248–49, 270–71, 274–75; Brian Hawkes: 66–67, 266–67; Darek Karp: 100–01; Yves Lanceau: 70–71, 74–75, 204–05, 208–09, 290–91.

Courtesy of Dianna Smith (www.pbase.com/comafungi): 34–35, 78–79, 110–11, 134–35, 138–39, 212–13, 220–21, 238–39, 242–43, 258–59, 294–95, 300–01, 304–05, 308–09, 312–13, 324–25, 336–37, 344–45, 356–57, 362–63; Anne Marie Roberts: 316–17.

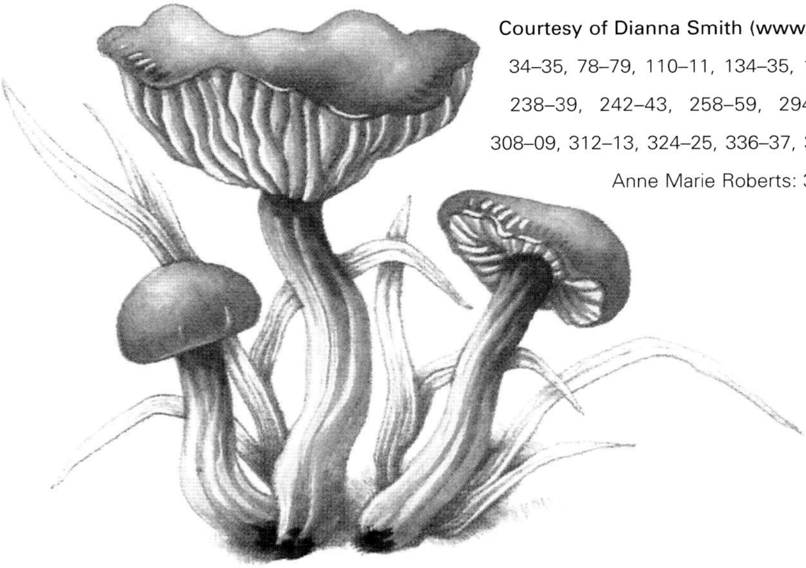

Index and Checklist

Keep a record of your sightings by ticking the boxes.